Resource Management in the Great Lakes Basin

Resource Management in the Great Lakes Basin

Edited by

F. A. Butrico
C. J. Touhill
I. L. Whitman

Battelle Memorial Institute

Heath Lexington Books
D. C. Heath and Company
Lexington, Massachusetts

Table of Contents

List of Tables

List of Figures

Preface

The Great Lakes—comprising the largest body of fresh water on earth—represent a natural resource of tremendous value to the two nations that share their shores. Such a resource deserves to be protected from such misuse and abuse as would prevent full realization of this value by society.

There have been many studies made on the Great Lakes Basin, dating back to the first comprehensive report on pollution of boundary waters issued by the International Joint Commission in 1918. Few have focused on the total system, failing to take into account the interrelationships among varied resource uses, alternative solutions, socioeconomic and institutional-political considerations, and technical innovation. Nor have these studies furnished useful vehicles for action.

It is believed that the concepts developed in this book represent a new approach to traditional resource management in the Great Lakes Basin. Also they are timely since in a number of Great Lakes states people are now being asked through bond issues to decide on the future of the Great Lakes, and considerable public and private funds will be spent on action programs without adequate intelligence to anticipate the results of these programs.

Acknowledgment

The material in this book was prepared by the staff of the Battelle Columbus and Battelle Northwest Laboratories of Battelle Memorial Institute supported by its President, Sherwood L. Fawcett. The effort is consistent with the Institute's philosophy of making meaningful contributions to the betterment of mankind. It is hoped that the approach and concepts developed will be useful to resource planners and managers and will advance the state of the art.

The Battelle staff members who made a contribution to the preparation of this book other than those already indicated on the title page and text included: D. G. Daniels, D. E. Olesen, A. J. Shuckrow and J. C. Sonnichsen, Jr.

Resource
Management
in the
Great Lakes
Basin

1 The Need for Research

Introduction

The water management complex of the Great Lakes represents a critical international problem of long-range significance. Although river basin planning and water resources management have developed with increasing sophistication and skill over the past three decades, the Great Lakes Basin presents a physical, economic, and political problem unlike any other in the world. The Lakes are an international resource serving an intensive complex of people and economic activities. And, more importantly, there is evidence that economic growth and technological change within the Basin have resulted in serious conflicts in the use of the Lakes' resources and serious deterioration of their natural qualities.

The Great Lakes System

The Great Lakes and St. Lawrence River system is one of the several great water systems which drain the North American continent toward its shores.

The principal source of water supply to the Great Lakes area is the precipitation over its water and land area. The average precipitation is about 31 inches per year, about two-thirds of which is returned to the atmosphere by evaporation and transpiration. The average net annual supply is, therefore, about 5×10^{13} gallons.

No existing system of manmade reservoirs anywhere in the world can compare with the Great Lakes for their water storage capabilities nor for their effect in regulating the flow of water as it passes through the system. However, the average inputs and outputs of the system are not continuous over time, so that variations in Lake levels occur, which is undesirable to at least the shoreline navigation and power interests.

At the present time, outflow from two of the Lakes is regulated. Lake Superior, the uppermost of the Great Lakes, has been regulated since 1921, when the natural riverbed of the St. Mary's River was dammed and the outflow controlled by a number of gates. At the same time, a lock system was installed to permit the movement of ships to and from Lake Superior.

Lake Ontario has been regulated since 1960 in accordance with the 1956 orders of the International Joint Commission. These orders essentially provided fixed-rule curves, with the aim of lowering high stages and raising low stages.

In 1965 the Corps of Engineers published a report on the regulation of all the Great Lakes in which, for the first time, the rule curves vary, depending on the antecedent rainfall and net water supply to the Basin. These plans were developed considering United States interests alone and are presently under study by the Canadian authorities.

Since many of the water resources problems are related to people, it should be noted that the Great Lakes region comprises an area of roughly 300,000 square miles, with a total population of 28 million which, in the next 50 years, is expected to grow to nearly 60 million, with a fivefold increase in water demand.[1] There are essentially four major zones of urbanization: Cleveland-Akron-Lorain; Windsor-Detroit-Flint; Toronto-Hamilton-Buffalo; and Chicago-Milwaukee.

Identification of Problems

Specific problems regarding the development and preservation of Great Lakes resources classified into six general areas of concern—water quality; water levels and interbasin transfer; ecological imbalances; institutional arrangements; economic; and social. The magnitude of these problems is illustrated by the costs for undertaking corrective measures. For example, to just depollute the Great Lakes will require the expenditure of over $8 billion. (Estimates made in the International Joint Commission report "Pollution of Lake Erie, Lake Ontario and the International Section of the St. Lawrence River-Volume I" (1969), including estimates for United States and Canadian expenditures for the control of municipal and industrial wastes.)

Water Quality

Virtually every activity man pursues modifies his environment in some way. While not all these modifications are detrimental, the overall result of human activity can be detrimental unless efforts are made to balance resource utilization against environmental quality. This balance must be sought with a full understanding of the interactions among resources, benefits, detriments, and long-range costs to society.

The current condition of the five Great Lakes demonstrates misuse and abuse of environment by man. One need only compare the rate of deterioration of water quality. Ranked according to impaired water quality or interference with beneficial uses, Lake Erie exhibits the greatest impairment, followed by Lakes Ontario, Michigan, Huron, and Superior. Population growth rates in the drainage basins around each of the Lakes correlate closely with the rate of deterioration in water quality in the Lakes.

The conclusion is inescapable—man is directly responsible for the accelerated deterioration of water quality. If corrective action is not taken, further deterioration will accompany future population growth (see Appendix A).

Water Levels and Interbasin Transfer

In the future, problems other than water quality are expected to be significant in the Great Lakes Basin. Quantity of water—as represented by reductions in inflows, potential reduction in outflow, and consequent variation in Lake levels—warrants considerable attention. The effects of variable or stable Lake levels on the ecology of the Lakes and on water and shoreline users are currently being investigated. Losses to users from reduced storage and outflows must be balanced by increases in water quality through reduced or diverted inflows.

Coinciding with the problem of levels, quantity, and flows, the Lake system is presently not well enough understood to evaluate the effects of major interbasin transfers of water, such as have already been proposed. Many engineers and planners envision continental water plans, extending from Alaska to Mexico, calling for massive transport of water and such major physiographic alterations as the damming up of the Rocky Mountain trench and of James Bay for storage of freshwater supplies. Needless to say, the Great Lakes figure prominently in most continental water plans, and the response of the Lake system to such herculean programs has serious implications which are presently unpredictable.

Ecological Imbalances

The beneficial water uses in the Great Lakes Basin are being seriously impaired by nuisance growths of aquatic organisms. The Lakes contain a constantly changing biological system composed of many microscopic and macroscopic life forms. These species are interrelated and depend on the condition of the total ecological balance of the environment for their existence. The biological system is dynamic, is complex, involves biochemical interrelationships among the life forms on the bottom and life forms in the water itself, and involves chemical and hydrologic interactions between the bottom sediments and the water. Factors that influence the aquatic ecological balance include: the concentrations of suspended and dissolved organic and inorganic compounds; the availability of these compounds as nutrient materials; the concentrations of dissolved gases including oxygen; and the availability of sunlight. (see Appendix B).

Institutional Problems

It has recently been recognized that policy and institutional questions often determine the course and eventual outcome of many water-related endeavors. It is quite revealing that, in this regard, the term institutional constraints is used most frequently to depict the roles played by various units of government. Constructive measures must be taken to ensure that governmental policies and arrangements no longer are constraining elements but provide, instead, opportunities for creative water management programs. Less is known and understood about creating successful water management institutions and intergovernmental arrangements than about any other facet of water quality management. Hence, it is clear that analysis of water resources policy and polity is needed to ensure that progress in these aspects of water management is commensurate with technological progress.

Economic and Social Problems

The Great Lakes provide a physical and environmental linkage in the development of regional water, land, mineral, and agricultural resources. Resource development and use require significant allocation of available financial resources, and hence pose a major economic problem: How might returns on resource development and management investments be maximized?

In time, as the development and use of natural resources in a region proceed, other problems arise related more to continued use than to initial development—problems which may exceed those of initial development in their significance and complexity. In the field of water resources there has evolved a body of economic theory and practice related to the development of river basins and other water resource systems, including development of benefit-cost theory and analyses, methods of selecting between alternative projects, determination of size and location of facilities, development of multiple-purpose projects and consideration of timing and sequence in project scheduling. At present, with the emergence of use problems, water and other natural resource economists are placing more attention on such matters as conflicts between water users, distribution of project benefits, economic externalities inherent in water development, social and environmental impacts, conservation, and the interaction between water resources and other contemporary needs—particularly urban planning and redevelopment. Although the water resources of the Great Lakes Basin are by no means fully developed at present, the major problems of concern to resource planners and managers are related to use, principally the satisfying of all types of water users' demand for the resource.

Financing

The costs of water management are high. There will be continuing need to study alternative methods of financing, including greater participation by the private sector and determination of equitable cost distribution as well as tax and incentive credits. The most significant problem at present is the financing of treatment facilities to improve water quality. Plans for adoption of water quality control measures have been based on the expectation that Federal support would be available under the provisions of the Clean Water Restoration Act of 1966. However, neither the Administration nor Congress has fulfilled the authorization for appropriations except for the initial year. The result has been a slowdown in the construction of treatment facilities, making it difficult to meet the nation's water quality goals by the original target date of 1972.

The construction grants aspects and other financing considerations will require investigation. For example, some have advocated that the cost of improving water quality should be considered social cost and, therefore, all society must share in paying the bill. If this concept is accepted, then there is need to develop methodology to evaluate and assign fair shares of the cost on the basis of such moral and practical factors as impact on the economy, ability to pay, and legal considerations. Still others advocate a pay-as-you-clean approach rather than the grant-in-aid procedure that makes today's citizen pay for tomorrow's treatment. If public funds remain in scarce supply, as can be anticipated because of higher priority uses, inflation, and other monetary considerations, these and other alternative proposals for financing must be considered.

Public Involvement

The complex issues of water resource management in the Great Lakes Basin and other basins will ultimately fall in the lap of the voting public. If the public is to decide the environment in which it wishes to live and must pay the bill, and if, truly, it is to participate in the decision-making process, a forum must be provided for interaction between conflicting sectors of the economy. An effective management program must lead to the generation of information, available to government and private sector alike, necessary for informed decision making on resource utilization at all levels of activity.

2

The Research Program

The objective of the study program is to consider together the causes and symptoms of the many complex problems concerned with effective planning and management of water and related land resources in the Great Lakes Basin. It requires using systems analysis techniques to construct models of the technical and economic factors to be considered in arriving at effective long-range management objectives. To make such models useful and effective, appropriate methodology should be developed together with the identification of new parameters for evaluating the social and economic values that are essential to making the best choice among alternatives. And, lastly, suitable alternatives should be developed for implementation of management programs through effective institutional arrangements and public involvement.

Research Philosophy

The program for managing the waters in the Great Lakes Basin reflects the changing nature of American society. It focuses sharply upon the instruments of human activity and achievement—the public and private institutions responsible for developing and maintaining natural resources and natural environment. Furthermore, programs of this kind would be the forerunner of a new generation of resource management—new because at last the causes of complex problems are to be identified and treated together with the symptoms.

Today's generation views coordination in resource management as highly sophisticated. In the future, coordination will be taken for granted because interactions between all management elements are measured and accounted for *during* the planning process, where planning interacts with the management—providing feedback to make resource management far more responsive to actual conditions and demands.

The planning management process must be viewed in this dynamic context—the study program structured as an integrated unit, comprising elements that can be isolated for descriptive purposes but not for the achievement of a breakthrough in the effectiveness of resource management. The program, as proposed in detail in this book, has many study components that would each have considerable merit in its own right. However, it is in their total interrelationship with one another that effective implementation of new concepts in resource management would be produced. This approach was emphasized recently by Congressman Emilio Q. Daddario (D.-Conn.) in a special report to the "Professional Engineer":

". . . . , let me suggest what I conceive to be the fundamental touchstones which must guide any technology assessment if it is to be adequate and useful. "These, in fact, are the four faces of technology assessment: 1) the physical, 2) the economic, 3) the social, and 4) the ethical. "If an undertaking in the assessment process should be completed without being responsive to the considerations demanded by each of these faces, in my view, it very likely will suffer from congenital defects."

Independence of Existing Programs

Since the study program is designed, in part, to measure the effectiveness of existing institutions on water management in the Basin, direction of the program must be largely independent of such existing agencies and organizations. Research on political mechanisms and institutional behavior would be difficult to undertake where the sponsoring agency was among those organizations being evaluated.

However, it should be pointed out that the study program in no way represents an attempt to supplant or reduce the authority of the existing institutional framework. In fact, it should be conducted within, and with full support of, existing agencies and programs in the Great Lakes Basin: Canadian, American, and joint.

Utilization of Available Research Resources

There are many related research studies currently underway or contemplated by universities, government agencies, and private laboratories. It is hoped the study herein described may serve as a blueprint around which all sponsors of research in the Great Lakes Basin can marshal their efforts. Such a blueprint may help conserve scarce research resources by avoiding excessive duplication of effort and may minimize the possibility of important research needs going unnoticed. The utilization of the combined university-based resources in the Basin is a concept suggested in reports emanating from several working conferences held in 1967 and 1968 by the University of Michigan and the Office of Water Resources Research, Department of the Interior.

Research Approach

The magnitude and complexity of the problems involved will require utilization of a high order of skills and technology. Using appropriate systems analysis techniques, models will be constructed of the technical and economic factors to be considered in arriving at effective long-range management objectives.

The full use and effectiveness of mathematical and simulation models are still dependent on the development of appropriate methodology for evaluating social and economic values and desires of the public. Therefore, provision is made for more effective assessment of the socioeconomic parameters that are essential to developing and making the best choice among alternative solutions.

The best of technical economics and socioeconomics would be of little value without effective institutional arrangements. All too often, desired proposals for improved water management practices have not been implemented because they failed to identify needed modifications in constraints imposed by existing water law, water management institutions, and water-use customs. The approach, therefore, is an interdependent analysis of the technological, social-economic, and institutional aspects.

Technical-Economic Analyses

**R. T. Jaske, C. E. Raines, N. L. Drobny,
W. A. Reardon, C. C. Coutant ***

There are two types of problems of major concern in the Great Lakes Basin. One type relates to the properties and characteristics of the resource, including problems of water quality (for example, eutrophication) and quantity (lake levels and outflows). The other type comprises problems related to the employment of resources, including construction and operation of facilities through which man interacts with and makes use of the Great Lakes resources. These problem areas are not independent and must be handled together within a unified systems framework.

A technical-economic analysis will require sizable financial and manpower resources, and it is imperative from the start that efforts be focused on those activities likely to yield significant returns. Mathematical modeling and related systems engineering activities are very complex, and if care is not taken to exclude all but the relevant parameters, their utility is greatly diminished. This requires a rather precise specification of the problem areas to be included in the various submodels, although flexibility would be provided for continuous updating.

A necessary element in developing a systems framework is the recognition of interactions inherent in resource utilization, both beneficial and destructive. It is not sufficient, for example, to state that water quality impairment resulting from waste disposal practices limits the utility of the Great Lakes for some other use, say water supply. Before one can explore alternative solutions or management policies, there is need to establish the location of the waste discharge, its physical and chemical characteristics, its behavior in the environment, and a great deal of other related information.

It is anticipated that the major interactions between various use categories will be antagonistic. Nevertheless, the probability of synergistic factors should not be ignored. For example, thermal discharges from power plants may in some areas have beneficial effects in terms of the promotion of conditions favorable to aquiculture.

Just as there are substantial interactions among the various elements of water resources development and utilization, there are notable interactions within each characteristic or property of the resource itself. In defining, for example, a water quality model for the Lakes, the effects of biological activity, physical phenomena such as currents and meterological effects, and a host of other interactions must be accounted for.

---

* Mr. Coutant is now with the Oak Ridge National Laboratories, Oak Ridge, Tennessee.

Specific Research Needs

The major research needs in technical economics related to a Great Lakes resource management program include:

(1) advanced basic research in field and laboratory data collection and analysis relating to limnological, chemical, ecological, and hydrologic factors in the Great Lakes resource complex;

(2) development of unified data format and data-handling systems, common computer languages, and improved information retrieval and dissemination capabilities;

(3) advances in the state-of-the-art in predictive technology for resource management-related activities, including physical, biological, and socioeconomic aspects; development of computer-based analytical and descriptive models;

(4) identification of alternative management options and the comparison of these options using predictive technology and new evaluative methods;

(5) development of new evaluative procedures for comparing alternative management plans, including consideration of economic and social criteria, and analyses of the impacts of technology on human affairs;

(6) development of better engineered solutions for achieving water management objectives, including new process development, structural innovation, and control of primary elements of the hydrologic cycle;

(7) capability in forecasting future industrial technology to be better able to determine directions in future water use and waste management options, particularly for manufacturing and energy-conversion industries; and

(8) utilization of new technological developments in computers, information handling, and communications to keep research and planning programs for resource management in the Great Lakes flexible and compatible with latest technologic capabilities.

Scope of the Research Program

The research program being developed relates in some manner to each of the eight major areas described above. However, the primary scope of the program described herein lies in items (3) developing predictive technology; (4) identifying and comparing management options; and (5) developing evaluative procedures.

It is these three functions which may be served through the development and employment of sophisticated, computer-oriented, analytical models. Relating to the other major areas, the study program would:

(1) assist in coordinating field and laboratory research needed to provide data in the analytical framework by providing a focus for the use of the data;

(2) provide uniform data format and initiate data-handling systems;

(3) disclose areas where better engineered solutions are needed and provide specifications and directions for their development;

(4) spur the improvement of predictive capability in forecasting industrial technology; and

(5) utilize new technological advances for research and planning (see Appendix D).

Predictive technology developed in the program would include the use of a hierarchy of simulation models developed for this purpose. These models are described in detail elsewhere in this section.

Evaluative procedures for comparing management options can be developed for inclusion in computer-oriented analytical models. Economic and social criteria are to form the focal point of this function and their development is in itself a major research undertaking described in the section on socioeconomic analysis. Another set of criteria relating to the impact of technology on human affairs can be derived through exploratory research.

Identification and testing of alternative management options for the Great Lakes represent, in a way, the primary product anticipated in such a study. Formation of these options will require close interaction among the technological, socioeconomic, and institutional functions within the entire research program.

Problems related to water quality modeling would receive the greatest emphasis because they are generally considered to be more difficult to handle than similar water quantity problems. This is because less is known about the multidimensional aspects of water quality phenomena and their interrelationships in large systems. In contrast, much more is known about the physical and engineering factors involved in the comprehensive management of water quantities in the Great Lakes and other large systems, and there exists a better statistical data base upon which to build. In general, modeling activities concerning physical and ecological aspects would be concentrated on the clarification of the quantity-quality interface which has preciously been neglected, primarily because of lack of data and incentive in terms of institutional policy.

In terms of the shoreline and related navigational and operational facilities, primary focal points will be physical facilities such as harbors, canals, locks, hydroelectric power facilities, industrial conversion and power industry development, and related public activities such as recreational facilities, municipal planning, shoreline real estate development, and land-based, water-oriented industries such as fisheries.

Further delineation of the term shoreline is of vast importance in definition of the scope of the computer simulation of the regional physical and economic interplay. Of necessity, the external boundaries of the system cannot be fully established at this time and may, in fact, require preliminary operation of the simulation systems in order to identify null points in product flow, economic interplay, and related socioeconomic activity in addition to the more obvious hydraulic and hydrological definitions of the Great Lakes drainage basin. Cognizance must be given to major external factors such as tributaries, diversion, basin-side land and resource utilization, and climatological factors which influence the Great Lakes. Further, the existence of engineered influences such as navigation locking, hydro peaking activity, and related systematic water uses must be fully related to other competing uses. This is especially important in the context of water quality, since a significant fraction of the water quality impairment in the Great Lakes stems from public and private waste-disposal practices throughout the Basin. Similarly, land-use patterns throughout the Basin govern the overall hydrologic response of the Basin and, thus, parameters of water quantity within the Great Lakes.

The Technical-Institutional Interface. A major step in the analysis of the technical factors related to management of Great Lakes water resources will be to specify, in at least preliminary terms, the interface relationships between technical-management options and institutional-management options. This is important since many problem areas that have already been identified, as well as those which remain to be identified, will require a combination of technical/institutional solutions or will at least have technical dimensions, the resolution of which will be institutionally dependent.

Two examples will serve to highlight the need for continuous feedback between activities in the technical and institutional sectors. There is little doubt that additional demands for power will develop in the Great Lakes area. It is also not difficult to imagine that technical analysis might in some cases favor hydropower plants over conventional thermal or nuclear plants, principally on the basis of thermal discharges and their potentially deleterious effect on the environment. However, although the possibility exists (technically) of extracting additional electric energy by hydro plants through additional Lake-regulation measures (including the possibility of pumped storage) and/or by the construction of additional plant capacity, further hydroelectric development on the Great Lakes system is, at present, largely constrained by international treaty. This situation exemplifies the strong, though not always recognized, ties between institutional and technical factors, and in this case on an international scale.

A second example, also having international implications, is related to the Chicago diversion from Lake Michigan. Acting as Special Master for the U.S. Supreme Court, Judge Albert B. Maris heard testimony revolving around the request by the City of Chicago to divert additional waters from Lake Michigan. On the basis of constitutional authority, international considerations, and technical factors, it was determined that no additional diversions would be permitted until it could be shown that every reasonable alternative for waste-water disposal had been exploited. Thus, technical responses to a given situation must be tailored to the existing institutional constraints. The institutional dependency of technical resource management options is derived from several factors.

(1) Users of Great Lakes resources often place conflicting and mutually exclusive demands on these resources. New institutions are likely to be needed to implement recommendations for resolving these conflicts based on a technical analysis of the tradeoffs involved. The above two examples illustrate the need for work in this area. Also, navigation and hydro power interests often conflict in periods when heavy demands are placed on commercial shipping (requiring high water levels) and when power demand is light, favoring low water levels. Currently lacking are both data on optimal policies for the combined management of the Great Lakes to provide these functions and institutional mechanisms whereby the conflicting interests can best work together to serve a common purpose.

(2) Water quality degradation, for example, need not occur either at the time or the place where potential pollutants are added. Consequently, the deleterious effects of pollution in most cases are not borne by the polluter. Often those who bear the brunt of pollution have no jurisdictional recourse *vis-á-vis* the polluter. These kinds of problems must be resolved by institutional systems.

(3) The Great Lakes environment has a finite natural capacity to assimilate waste materials. Sound resource management policy dictates that this finite capacity be fully utilized. However, in areas where waste loadings exceed this capacity, one is faced with the problem of allocating this assimilative capacity among existing users. The conventional approach is to require uniform waste treatment of all discharges. However, it has been shown for many situations that other policies for allocating the natural assimulative capacity among users may be more prudent in terms of resource management. Current institutions, however, do not provide mechanisms for enforcing other than uniform treatment standards.

No means exist whereby one political entity may be compensated for and hence motivated to assume responsibility for what might appear on the surface to be a disproportional share of the problem for the long-run common benefit of all concerned. For example, it has been stated that the current phosphate load to Lake Erie of 137,000 lb/day should be reduced to 9000 lb/day. Technical analysis can be used to establish the consequences of various phosphate loads and determine the most prudent points to remove these pollutants (based on economics and other factors). It is likely that existing institutional frameworks will not be adequate for implementing the solution.

The instances given above are only examples of situations requiring an integrated institutional-technical approach in developing solutions. The purpose in defining them early in the research program would be to provide focus for the activities to be conducted in the institutional sector.

Analytical Methodologies

The objectives of this study program for the prudent management of the Great Lakes water and related land resources require that computational methodology be available which will (1) help identify the substance of the alternative management options and (2) permit the evaluation in advance of the impact of alternative policies prior to full-scale implementation on the full regional system.

The power of the computer in greatly enhancing complex analysis through the applications of algebraic linguistics and numerical analysis has become very great. However, a much greater potential lies in those areas of science and engineering that are beyond the scope of today's formal mathematics. The impact of this is being evidenced by the efforts of engineers to use computers in complex systems involving human organizations. Progress in this direction is somewhat inhibited by the lack of adequate mathematical or linguistic concepts.

The program concept provides an unparalleled opportunity for the technical community to join with the political community in the development of significant advances in the field of information science. Much of the failure to communicate in the modern era is related to the breakdown in information flow involving the structure of formal mathematics as it exists today. These mathematical forms, such as the calculus, exhibit great power in the structuring of quantitative concepts. For example, in the fields of chemistry and physics, the natural phenomena observed have sufficient simplicity or restrictions that concise theoretical concepts can be based upon precise logical thought and formal mathematics. Beyond this, the scientist has turned to the general area of stochastic mathematics, finding fewer restrictions in the informational relationships to which the postulates apply. However, it is relatively unsuited to the structuring of powerful analytical concepts.

The use of simulation, where the fundamental logic principles are indefinitely structured, permits a ready survey of a sufficient range of the unknown parameters in each case by extensively correlating model behavior with available real system behavior. Life and social science studies characteristically deal with dynamic unstable systems which are extremely difficult to reproduce in an experimental situation. The informational relationships so far obtainable indicate very complex conceptual models for which tremendous amounts of information are required.

The suggested research strategy, therefore, becomes one of acquiring, analyzing, searching, and model building at a vastly increased level of physical speed and complexity. However, examination of the physical interactions of each of these processes upon the others reduces the amplitude of the problem by early identification of the significance of inputs or subparameters. The role that computers play in the enlargement of the scope of the iterative planning process can be very great. In its ultimate application, hierarchy of models could be completely equivalent to the development of a language and, therefore, more comprehensive than a mathematical theory based solely on today's limited formal mathematics.

With this background, and thoughtful projection to the future, the application of the general field of predictive technology can be developed in some detail.

Delineation of the Hierarchical System. The development of analytical methodologies is fundamental to the concept of a systems approach to a problem. The basic need is for a family or hierarchy of model systems or internal language media which can, within the accuracy constraints imposed by the input information, predict consequences of potential actions. The aim is to manipulate the controllable inputs to the system so as to identify desirable outputs in both quality and quantity. This is represented conceptually in Figure 2-1.

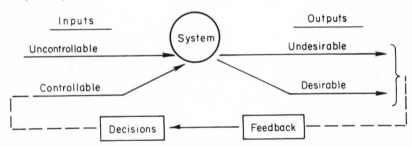

Figure 2-1. Basic Systems Concept

The following statements guide the development of the system of subprograms which are discussed in the text to follow.

(1) A hierarchical modeling approach would be applied from the outset in order to yield an operational preliminary linked model at the conclusion of the proposed program.

(2) Each step in the use of the models and projections of the effects and concurrent estimates of capital and operating costs of alternative proposals would be clearly related to the end purpose in order to create a useful tool early in the development and at phased stages in the progress toward operational status.

(3) Appropriate subprojects would be developed centering around subsystems such as algal response, food chains, and systems size.

(4) Interactions with economics models would be introduced early and in keeping with the level of hierarchical format.

The hierarchical systems analysis approach is an efficient method of obtaining operationally adequate simulation models for complex problems. The only requirement placed on the description of individual phenomena in the top echelon model is that of scope adequacy. Lower echelon models are employed to explore individual phenomena in more detail and at varying levels of activity, perhaps utilizing more rigorous mathematical representations as the scale of modeling moves downward to the more deterministic scope. Valid simplifications are sought, such that the highest echelon models do not bog down in unnecessary detail in a subarea. This permits the top echelon model to be comprehensive in an empirically valid fashion; otherwise, programs that are developed by connecting subprograms become so cumbersome and inefficient that they cannot be used (even if computer core capabilities are not exceeded). This objective is a guiding policy of the system development so that the specialist is kept fully oriented to the fact that individual details of lower levels appear in simplified or simulated form in the higher levels.

Alternatives to the use of simulation for lower levels of investigation (hierarchically speaking) are mathematical analysis, experimentation with the actual system, and reliance upon experience and intuition. All, including simulation, have limitations. Mathematical analysis of complex systems is, as stated above, very often impossible; experimentation with actual or pilot systems is costly, time consuming, and often impracticable. Intuition and experience are often the only alternatives to computer simulation, but these have been shown by the existing situation in resources management to be most inadequate.

Simulation problems are characterized by being mathematically intractable and in having resisted solution by analytical methods. The problems usually involve many variables, many parameters, functions which are not well behaved mathematically, and random variables. Much effort is now devoted to computer simulation because of its ability to produce practical answers for difficult problems.

Continuous-Change and Discrete-Change Models. It is convenient to classify simulation models into two major types: continuous-change models and discrete-change models. Advances in computational machinery indicate that this distinction will become blurred as a new generation of analog-digital hybrid systems is brought into general use for scientific computation.

Continuous-change models are appropriate when the analyst considers the system as a rate-oriented continum rather than a succession of individual items. These models are usually characterized by differential or difference equations that describe rate of change of the variables with respect to time. In such models, which have long been used in the physical sciences and engineering, the researcher uses analytical or numerical techniques to solve the system of equations. If no such available technique is powerful enough or appropriate, the analyst adopts simulation. Continuous-change models are naturally suited to electronic or mechanical analog computation. Pure analog machines have the disadvantage of being impracticable if (1) the functions are discontinuous; (2) the number of variables is very large; (3) some of the variables are random variables; or (4) there are other inherent machine limitations.

Continuous-change models can be simulated on digital computers by using finite-difference equations which, in the limit, approach the differential equations of continuum. The user selects as the state variables the primary factors of interest. The formulation of a continuous-change model consists of (1) identifying the state variables, the exogenous variables, and the parameters and (2) developing the functional relationships. The result of the computations is a table or graph representing state vectors as a function of time or summaries of these data.

Discrete-change models, on the other hand, use changes in the state of the system at discrete intervals rather than over a continuum. Systems are idealized as network flow systems and are characterized by the following:

(1) the system contains components (elements or subsystems) each of which performs definite and prescribed functions;

(2) items flow through the system, from one component to another, requiring the performance of a function at a component before the item can move on to the next component; and

(3) components have finite capacity to process the items and, therefore, items may have to wait before reaching a particular component.

The main objective of discrete-change systems is to carry out analyses of problems which involve questions of capacity of the system, that is, how many items will pass through the systems in a given period of time as a function of the structure of the system. The analytical techniques which may be used to solve such problems are queuing theory and stochastic processes. Examples of problems which have been formulated and studied as discrete-change models are communication networks, logistics systems, traffic systems, and budget models for rivers and estuaries which are being developed for the purpose of relating a large number of simultaneous events.

The computation in this type of simulation consists to a large extent of keeping track (housekeeping) of individual items at all times, moving them from waiting lines to components, timing the necessary processing or functional transformations, and removing and transporting the items to other components or waiting lines. The result of a simulation run is a set of statistics describing the behavior of the simulated system during the run.

Stochastic Aspects. The hierarchy of models will be designed to be implemented in computer simulation runs using either a deterministic or a Monte Carlo procedure. A typical application would be the use of one or more of the primary physical models of lake limnology in a set of runs to represent a statistical sample of the universe of forcing functions acting upon the lake system (wind speed, wind direction, solar and sky radiation, local contaminant loading, and so on). In order to reduce the total number of runs where improbable sets of coincident behavior would occur, the simulation would be controlled by stored and repeatable forcing functions which would be derived from real data. The design of these forcing functions is crucial to the realism of the outputs of proposed simulations, the validity of models, and their utility in the intended purpose.

Increasing use of a combination of stochastic inputs organized to be a part of deterministic computations is being made by researchers in large-scale simulations. For example, in modeling the extent of an algal bloom which would be sufficiently large to cause a major reduction in dissolved oxygen, attention must be given to a number of stochastic factors in addition to the mechanical forces involved in the transport of the biomass. These would be (1) the extent of clouding and cloud density; (2) uniquely high water temperature; and (3) sufficiently high concentrations of key nutrients (phosphorus, carbon dioxide, vitamins, dissolved oxygen, and so on), some of which result from primary bacterial action on wastes stochastically entering the lake. In order to obtain seasonally correlated functional descriptions of many of the dependent variables in the model system, it would be necessary that the forcing function be designed to permit realistic distribution of occurrences over extended time periods.

Such models permit undertaking quality and development management studies not only to arrive at controls over time-averaged or instantaneous values of water-quality variables, but also to evaluate the importance of the degree of control over the time variance of inherent and artificial pollution loading.

Preliminary Concept of Model Framework

Development of the framework and substance of the various echelons in the overall simulation-model hierarchy will be perhaps the single most important technical activity in this study program. A hierarchical simulation model (containing linked submodels) will be developed that will provide the flexibility of investigating certain effects on a micro (sublake) basis, or a macro (basin-wide) basis, depending upon the questions to be answered. This flexibility will be incorporated by so structuring the model that one can operate selected portions of a given echelon or, alternatively, by activating appropriate cross linkages, operate larger and larger portions of the overall model. The major advantage of this approach is that as one progresses to higher and higher echelons in the hierarchy, the required detail is reduced by using empirically validated simplifications of various phenomena. Validation is achieved on the lower echelon where the phenomenon is explored in detail. Another advantage of this approach is the efficiency achieved by not having to activate the entire model to explore local phenomena.

Utilizing the scheme shown in Figure 2-1, a top echelon model for the Great Lakes system is shown in Figure 2-2. Note that the system consists

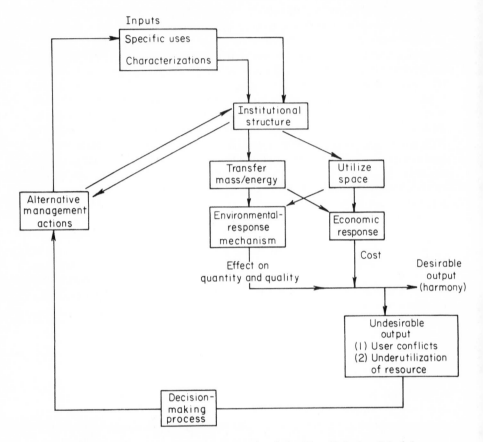

Figure 2-2. Analytical Framework of the Top Echelon Model

of the environmental response mechanisms, the economic response mechanisms, and the institutional structure. The present state-of-the-art of simulation is such that the suggestion of mathematically simulating institutional, environmental, and economic responses should not be construed as a naive viewpoint but rather an anticipation of improvements through this program and others over the next several years.

Institutional and economic responses are described elsewhere, while the following discusses environmental responses and the automation of the decision-making process.

As shown in Figure 2-2 inputs to the overall simulation model describe basically the uses one might wish to make of the Great Lakes water and related land resources. In a fundamental sense these uses may be of two types: (1) to transfer mass (that is, matter) and/or energy to, from, or within the Lakes; and (2) to occupy space or surface area on the watershed, the shoreline, or the water surface. The advantage of structuring the model in terms of these fundamental inputs (as opposed to conventional use categories such as water supply, navigation, and so on) is that it will maximize flexibility in the model to accommodate uses which may not yet be conceived.

Inputs in the mass/energy-transfer category are listed below and may reflect inputs imposed directly on the Lakes, such as waste discharge through a lake outfall, or may include inputs which reach the lakes by rather indirect means, such as runoff or tributary flow. It should also be noted that some of these inputs will be controllable (for example, waste discharge), while others will be essentially noncontrollable (for example, precipitation).

Mass

Water
Organic compounds exerting BOD
Nutrients (primarily nitrogen and phosphorus)
Silts
Oils
Pesticides
Coliform bacteria
Inorganic salts

Energy

Thermal
Kinetic (wind, etc.)
Gravitational
Chemical (including biochemical).

Figure 2-3 illustrates the next lower echelon representation of only the environmental subsystem. The orbital concept shown illustrates water as the core, matter or energy components that may be present in water in varying degrees in the first orbit, and those factors that exert boundary influences on the system in the second ring. In addition, the response mechanism or factor relating cause (second orbital) to the intrinsic nature of the water particle is a function of both natural alteration and manmade or engineered innovation.

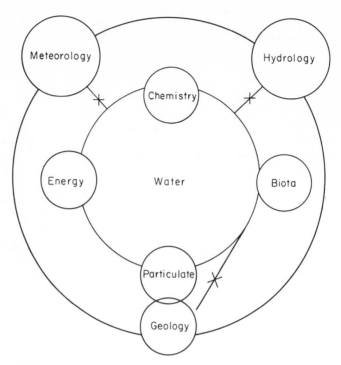

Figure 2-3. Schematic Representation of Environmental Subsystem

Figures in Appendix C show in more detail the elements affecting two of the properties (chemistry and biota) shown in the first orbital of Figure 2-3. These box diagrams represent still lower echelons and are the basis from which the overall model can be built up. On this level of the hierarchy, the specialist and the analyst are encouraged to explore the phenomena in great detail. A model at this level might fully utilize a present day large-scale computer. The extensive investigation at this level will permit development of simplified representation for use on a higher echelon. Appendix C gives a detailed description of the phenomena portrayed and preliminary ideas of how they might be modeled.

The extent to which a single environmental subsystem might be used to model regional or macro problems is at present unknown. The limitations will undoubtedly be governed by the complexity of the particular area under examination. Therefore, within a specific lake there might exist as few as one or as many as 100 separate subsystems. As the dimensionality of the subsystems increases, a means of linking the interdependence must be achieved. Appropriate linkage for the given situation would be obtained by providing for some sort of transport mechanism. This transport mechanism could be either discrete or continuous in nature.

Figure 2-4 give a schematic representation of three separate subsystems within some arbitrary body of water. Transport from one environmental subsystem to another can occur by one of three ways: (1) direct transport of water between cores; (2) transport of water between first orbitals through the property of energy exchange; and (3) transport of water from cell or first orbital to the second orbital in the form of evapotranspiration (meterorology) or channel flow (hydrology). In transporting water directly between cores, the transport mechanism would, under most circumstances, be discrete. Under these circumstances, a Markov or Monte Carlo technique would be employed. It is suggested that the second type of transport (between first orbitals) could be accomplished using a continuous method of analysis. The motion of the transported material would render itself as kinetic energy, and therefore feedback to the first orbital would be necessary to employ fundamental relationships. The third type of transport which could be accommodated would be from the core or first orbital to the second orbital of the exchanging environmental subsystem. Transport from the center core to the outer or second orbital of the subsequent subsystem would be in the form of discrete methodology, whereby transport from the first orbital to the second orbital of an adjoining subsystem would be continuous in nature.

This approach of linking together environmental subsystems can be ultimately extended to include the entire basin under consideration. This would be the highest echelon within the technical sector of the proposed research program. Figure 2-5 schematically represents this concept; it was constructed assuming discrete linking through core elements. Only the major transport mechanism between these bodies of water has been presented at this time.

Simulation of the many aspects of the entire Great Lakes resources system is feasible using this approach. Utilization of the hierarchical concept provides assurance of the development of a succession of credible simple models, since during the evolution, salient phenomena are treated in whatever detail necessary at the appropriate level.

Validation of Model

Simulation models will have to be extensively validated, and the output as well as the input data will require specific levels of accuracy, depending on the sensitivity of the effects of a given parameter. Since there is a reluctance on the part of some investigators to fully accept the results of a simulation even though the numerical results are highly indicative of success, it is incumbent upon the simulation model technology to develop

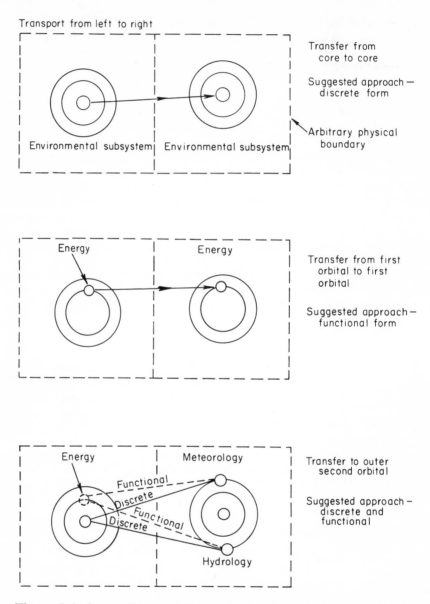

Figure 2-4. Some Types of Transport between Environmental Subsystems

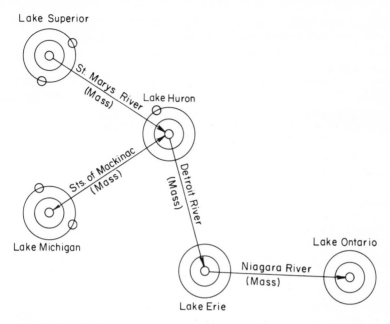

Figure 2-5. Schematic Representation of Linking in the Highest Echelon Model

means of testing the accuracy of the methodology in a fully auditable and meaningful way.

Four important criteria for satisfaction must be considered:

—Were the data measured in a standard manner and was the population sampled representative of the entire sample?

—Were the mathematical tests which were applied sufficiently objective to preclude built-in bias or subjectivity?

—Would the model system be subject to exterior bias such as sabotage, electronic malfunction, or inquiry from unauthorized persons without having the ability to detect or abort such influences?

—Is the use of electronic simulation, with the possibility of compensating error, ever tractable in terms of legal or quantitative proof in cases involving institutional systems such as law where statistics are often inadmissible in testimony?

The answers to the first three questions lie in adoption of strict and rigorous in-house rules regarding the validity and quality of input data and the development of rapport between and among the scientific community and the developers of the hierarchical model system. It would be essential to have built-in checking procedures such as specialized applications of statistical tests. However, in the last analysis, there is no substitute for appropriate rapport among developers and users of a system and the successful completion of some subprograms which are effective.

In regard to the last question, it would be considered as a fundamental objective of the system to investigate the institutional arrangements in a manner in which reforms in the use of testimony could be achieved. Progress in the use of computer models in the management of court dockets, data processing of evidence, and related technical advances show promise of long-term acceptability by society at large of the use of electronic media for advanced information exchange. However, progress will not come rapidly, and the original model system will of necessity require extensive progress under existing institutional arrangements.

The following steps are considered essential in the development of a valid model subsystem or master system:

—a complete inventory of the literature, including contract reports and in-house data, even if unpublished in the usual sense, concerning some aspect of the environment or similar sample environments;

—formulation of a preliminary model from existing data and best estimates with *due consideration of error limits* on all input data;

—use of the preliminary model to guide acquisition of additional field data of highly specific form and accuracy;

—use of this improved and specifically oriented data to improve the values of coefficients of the comprehensive model system and to design experiments of limited scope;

—quantitative predictions of increasingly larger sectors of the limnological or economic environment and performance of large-scale tests of the system in which the public is involved; and

—use of the validated technical model system in the investigation of institutional arrangements, with feedback relevant to additional improvement.

It would be expected that each of these steps could be carried forward in an organized manner with frequent opportunities for internal and external review. A guiding rule of the programming of the system would be the requirement that the system be capable of operation with alternative subsystem models or computer codes at the option of individual projects. In this manner, research could be performed on the research tool itself on a continuing basis without the need to interrupt the progress of operational use of the system. This approach is fundamentally the same as that used in the development of shared time systems and analogous to the checking and quality assurance procedures involved in the fine instrument and aerospace fields.

An example of the development of a successful simulation subsystem is the Battelle-managed work for the Atomic Energy Commission in the simulation of the thermal effects of artificial modifications of the natural regimes caused by dams, industry, and other parametric variations. This model is called COL HEAT and has been described in the open literature.[1]

Frequent testing of the concept with real data under rigorously controlled conditions of data validity have led to the comparison of predicted and actual stream flow temperatures shown in Figure 2-6. Despite this close agreement and statistical checks which indicated that the model was faithfully reproducing the desired temperature regime of the Columbia River with 95 percent confidence, additional tests on a small, completely isolated system were authorized. The system selected was the Deerfield River in Massachusetts, with a nominal flow of about one-fortieth that of the Columbia River system. The results of this test clearly show that the computation system is fully capable of bridging the quantity gap and can reproduce time-variant estimates of water quality parameters in widely differing river systems with equal reliability. At this point, the use of the model was authorized for increasingly complex and larger systems, such as the Illinois Waterway, the Upper Mississippi River drainage area, and the Ohio River drainage area. At the current state of development, COL HEAT forms an ideal systems base for the further development into chemical transport, oxygen modeling, and related ecologically involved subsystems.

With respect to the case of the Great Lakes, a similar series of validations would be expected to take place. These would include use of the preliminary master system model to simulate a variety of past occurrences in both time dependence and magnitude. The results of these validations would suggest areas in which additional data were needed. Thus, the buildup of confidence in the system would proceed by a simultaneous usage of the preliminary models while improved data and procedures were under examination and intensive testing. Ultimately, large field tests involving a relatively large subsystem, such as a small experimental lake or a well-known economic subregion, could be subjected to controlled variation in order to test the response of the simulation prediction. Full application of many technologies, such as the use of radioactive tracers or activation analysis of material involved in transport mechanisms, would be employed in order to test such Monte Carlo events as food-chain mechanisms from lower to higher organisms and related trade-off phenomena. While the example given is a relatively simple one in comparison with large input-output models used for economic research, the principles are much the same. Extremely large systems, such as the AEC-sponsored Nuclear Power Economy model, which involve the combined operation of subsystems at both Battelle's Pacific Northwest Laboratory and Oak Ridge National Laboratory are excellent prototypical examples. Many others could be cited.

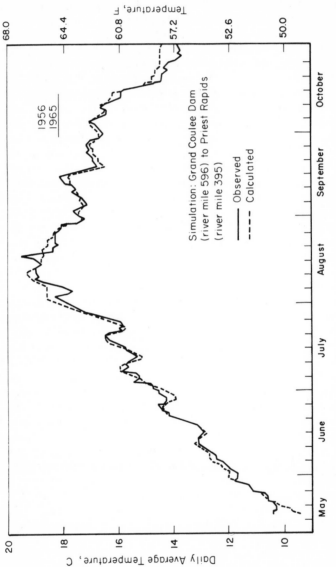

Figure 2-6. Comparison of Measured Versus Simulated Temperatures at Priest Rapids Dam after Transport from Grand Coulee Dam (196 Miles)

Socioeconomic Analyses

B. W. Cone, S .E. Goldstone, G. L. Nehman

Socioeconomic analyses may be viewed as the linkages between technological analyses on the one hand and institutional analyses on the other. Information on the nature of the physical world and how it might conceivably be modified by technology is taken as a basic input. Through economic analyses, this basic input is transformed into information that can be used directly by public decision makers. More specifically, the analyses will develop information needed to answer two basic questions about prospective Great Lakes programs: What programs should be undertaken? How should they be financed?

A key and perhaps unique feature of this type is that they will be institutionally free. That is, the analyses will be carried out without any preconceived notions about what institutions will be involved. Under this ground rule, alternatives need not be eliminated purely because they are feasible or desirable from the standpoint of a particular agency or a particular jurisdiction. The analyses can be much broader in range than would be possible if they were carried out in a limited institutional context. The information developed can be useful not only to public decision makers in existing institutions but also to prospective public entrepreneurs who are interested in developing new institutional arrangements.

What Programs Should Be Undertaken

Determining what programs should be undertaken is a two-step process involving first the generation and then the evaluation of a set of alternatives. Although this process appears to be straightforward in principle, in practice it is fraught with difficulties. Many of these difficulties are due directly to limitations in the state of the art of economic analysis and measurement. From a practical standpoint, however, the most serious difficulties are attributable to institutionally related limitations of the kind that this study will be specifically designed to overcome. These difficulties pertain to both the generation and evaluation phases of the analysis.

Generation of Alternatives. Most of the literature on economic program analyses deals with the problems of how alternatives should be evaluated. From a practical standpoint, however, the problem of alternative *generation* is equally, if not more important, than evaluation. The best alternative cannot be selected if it is never considered! One must conclude that the lack of attention to this phase of program analyses is due not to its unimportance but rather to the fact that not much is known about how to improve it.

In order to improve the alternative generation process it is necessary to first diagnose the reasons why difficulties occur. In the realm of governmental or public decision making, fundamental difficulties are not hard to identify. The heart of the problem is embedded in the structure of the political process.

To start with, most individuals in society have some configuration of wants relating to publicly supplied goods and services. If each individual on his own attempted to express these wants in the form of demands on his public representatives, the political process would break down. Representatives would be burdened with tremendous input overloads. This excess burden in all likelihood would produce chaos and a general inability of governmental bodies to act. Every political system, in order to maintain its viability, must, therefore, develop the means for coping with and preventing this potential overload.[2]

One basic method used in our society for preventing this kind of overload is the collection and combination of a large number of individual but closely related demands into organized interest groups. Thus, around each possible use of water, associations of persons particularly interested in that use tend to be formed. These private associations then seek to have governmental responsibility for the water use they are interested in vested in a separate agency to which they have special access and in which they have confidence. In response to this pressure, the general tendency has been to establish a governmental bureaucratic structure which closely parallels the structure of private-interest groups. Paralleling the private commercial fishing interests we have the Bureau of Commercial Fisheries; paralleling the sport fishing interests, the Bureau of Sport Fisheries; paralleling the host of private conservation-oriented organizations, the Federal Water Quality Administration; paralleling such private organizations as the National Rivers and Harbors Congress and the National Waterways Association, the Corps of Engineers; and so on.[3]

This form of bureaucratization, which so closely parallels the structure of private interest groups, has several effects. On the positive side, it facilitates the communication of demands from private citizens to their public representatives. This should make a government's decisions and outputs more responsive to the desires of its citizens. On the negative side, such a structure leads to bureaus which are assigned to particular programs rather than to general objectives. Authority relating to general objectives is fragmented and divided among a number of different bureaus. Since no particular bureau has jurisdictional authority or capability to examine a wide range of alternatives for achieving general objectives, many highly desirable alternatives may never be considered. In areas such as water resource development, which involve a high degree of technological interdependence and conflict between different kinds of uses, the practical consequences of this restricted range of analyses may be particularly severe.

A recent case study by Robert Davis provides a dramatic illustration of the practical consequences of restricting the range of alternatives.[4] In 1963 the Corps of Engineers developed a comprehensive water resource plan for the Potomac River.[5] Part of this plan, which was subsequently analyzed by Davis, was aimed at maintaining the level of water quality. In operational terms the Corps chose the objective of maintaining a minimum monthly average dissolved oxygen level of 4 mg/l. Keeping dissolved oxygen above this level would provide some assurance that the upper estuary would be hospitable to fish. The Corps recommended that the objective be achieved by means of low flow augmentation at a total present value cost of 115 million dollars. (The total recommended plan of water systems served several purposes other than maintaining water quality. This figure represents the increment in total costs that is attributable to low-flow augmentation. It is the present value of these costs over a 50-year period discounted at 4 percent.)

Davis, in his subsequent analysis, found that the same objective could be achieved by a combination of mechanical reoxygenation and low flow augmentation at a total cost of only 22 million dollars. Moreover, he found that several other alternatives involving various waste treatment processes showed similar potential for substantial cost savings. Despite the overwhelmingly large cost savings that these alternatives would make possible, they were never considered in the initial planning study.

Davis claims that "a large part of the failure to consider alternatives is attributable to institutional factors." [6] Several factors were involved. First, the limited jurisdiction of the Corps played a part. The Corps has authority to improve water quality through low flow augmentation, but it does not have the authority to achieve this same objective through treatment of wastes. Authority for the latter rests largely with local and state governments and to some extent with the Federal Water Quality Administration (FWQA). Corps planners, understandably, are not likely to view as practical alternatives that require the coordination of a number of outside agencies over which they have no control.

Second, as a consequence of its past history, the Corps has developed a strong capability and orientation toward structural alternatives. It therefore has a strong vested interest in avoiding nonstructural alternatives such as reoxygenation. Beyond this, reoxygenation, as well as some of the other alternatives not considered by the Corps, is a relatively new technique for dealing with water quality problems. It is very likely that Corps planners were not sufficiently familiar with these techniques to consider them as feasible alternatives.

Finally, the Corps may well have been motivated to restrict the range of alternatives considered because of institutional rigidities related to financing. Under the Water Quality Act of 1951, low flow augmentation used for purposes of water quality improvement receives 100 percent financing by the Federal government. Alternatives relating to waste treatment facilities, in contrast, receive no such Federal subsidization. Under the Water Quality Act of 1965, reimbursement to municipalities for waste treatment is limited to no more than 55 percent. At the time of the Corps study, the amount of reimbursement available would have been even less. Table 2-1 shows the consequences of the current financing arrangements. The low flow augmentation system, despite the fact that it is five times more costly in total, is still the low cost alternative from the standpoint of the local communities involved. In order to have its plan approved by Congress, the Corps would require the political support of these local communities. Because of this they may justifiably have viewed alternatives that did not take advantage of the 100 percent subsidized low flow augmentation approach as politically unfeasible.

Table 2-1.

Total and Local Costs of Alternative Systems for Maintaining Dissolved Oxygen Levels in the Potomac River (Millions of Dollars)

System	Total Costs	Costs to Area
Reoxygenation and low-flow	22	14
Low-flow augmentation	115	0

Source: Davis, op. cit., Table 24, p. 125.

This discussion illustrates the kinds of difficulties that typically hamper the alternative generation phase of economic analyses. Battelle's diagnosis suggests that these difficulties are largely due to the narrow institutional contexts within which such studies take place. These difficulties can be overcome in two ways. First, the study need not be conducted under the auspices of limited institutional sponsorship. Second, as an integrated part of a comprehensive study, the economics analysts could be part of a working team which includes technical specialists who are familiar with a broad spectrum of technological alternatives. This interaction between economics analysts and technical specialists will be designed to stimulate awareness not only of techniques that are currently operational, but also of new techniques that might be feasibly developed if they showed sufficient economic promise. Whether or not a new technique shows such promise may be determined in the evaluation phase of the analysis.

Evaluation of Alternatives. Having identified an array of alternatives, the next step will be to compare and evaluate them. This will be accomplished by applying the techniques of benefit-cost analysis. The analysis will be aimed at providing the maximum amount of useful information possible for choosing, from among the candidate alternatives, those that will produce the most economic benefits relative to their costs.

Analyzing the benefits and costs of alternative programs, especially in relation to the very complicated Great Lakes system, is, to use an old phrase, easier said than done. The task in all its dimensions is an immense one and it is beset with practical difficulties. There is the problem discussed at some length in the section on institutional analyses—that from a practical standpoint it is not enough to determine the overall level of economic costs and benefits. It is also necessary to know how these will be distributed among different groups and different areas. If many different jurisdictions have to be brought together to implement a particular program, the political costs may outweigh the net economic benefits. How different groups will be affected depends, of course, not only on what programs are undertaken but also on how they are financed. Therefore, discussion of questions relating to distribution effects are deferred until the subsequent discussion on financing arrangements.

Irrespective of how they are distributed, just estimating the total costs and benefits is extremely difficult. The following threefold research strategy might be considered to deal with these difficulties:

(1) First, developing a series of computer models to simulate the relevant underlying physical phenomena and how they can be expected to respond to the different alternatives under consideration. In connection with the water quality problem, for example, develop a model to simulate the response of various water quality parameters indices in different parts of the Great Lakes to different configurations of waste treatment and discharge. The development of this and other physical models is discussed in the preceding section on technical economic analysis.

(2) Using the physical simulation models as basic inputs and cost analysis, determine the relationship between costs and physical performance. Two kinds of questions can be answered. First, an attempt to determine the low-cost methods of achieving selected fixed levels of performance. Second, by considering the low-cost alternatives for different levels of physical performance estimate the incremental costs of achieving incremental performance.

(3) In parallel and interacting with the cost analysis, measure the magnitude of economic benefits that would be produced by varying levels of physical performance. Preliminary rough estimates of benefits will help focus the cost analysis onto the economically reasonable range of performance levels. To the extent possible, more sophisticated techniques can then be used to obtain more refined benefit estimates. As in the cost analysis, estimates can be made of the incremental benefits that are associated with incremental cost estimates. It will be possible to select program objectives in terms of operational measures of physical performance

which will not be too far, it is hoped, from maximizing overall net benefits. In addition, this method can achieve a range of choice in the ultimate selection of suitable alternatives.

What does this type study promise that other studies have not already accomplished? A recent study done by the Federal Water Quality Administration provides an excellent example for illustrating this point.[7] This study was aimed at developing a plan for controlling water quality in Lake Erie. It is especially significant here because it provides some very useful background material on one of the most urgent problems in the Great Lakes.

Before the FWQA study was undertaken, the 1965 Lake Erie Enforcement Conference required that secondary treatment be provided at all municipalities by 1972. The FWQA, because of this, started out with the presumption that secondary treatment together with phosphorus removal would be a minimum program. Using available cost formulas, the FWQA estimated that the immediate construction costs for this minimum program, to handle expected growth through 1990 would be approximately 1.3 billion dollars. Another 1.4 billion dollars would be required after 1990. The estimated costs and benefits of this minimum program, along with the three other more costly alternatives examined by the FWQA, are shown in Table 2-2. By itself, the minimum program while it would improve the water quality in the lake, would not eliminate all problem areas. This can be accomplished for an estimated additional 1.3 billion dollars by introducing advanced treatment at 67 plants, that is, Program B. FWQA recommends this above the minimum program because under it "swimming and fishing—which are now restricted activities—will increase to near their full potential, and . . . the destructive pollution pace will be greatly diminished, giving the natural self-purification phenomena a chance to bring Lake Erie to a much more desirable state." [8]

A major virtue of this study is that it presents several alternative programs aimed at different levels of performance. And with each of these program levels there is an estimate of the incremental costs as well as a rough specification of the benefits. There are, however, three basic kinds of information gaps in the study that the analysis proposed here would be aimed at filling. These are as follows:

(1) As it stands, the relationship between the different programs and the water quality results that will be achieved is ambiguous. Program A will produce improved water quality, Program B will allow swimming and fishing near their full potential, and so on. The FWQA was unable to be more precise in discussing these results largely because of the lack of available information on how water quality indices can be expected to respond to reductions in waste discharges. Under this proposal a physical simulation model of water quality response of the Lake will be devised to fill this information gap.

Table 2-2.
Cost-Benefit Summary of Alternative Programs for Improving Water Quality of Lake Erie

Program	Construction Costs, billions of dollars			Incremental Per Capita Annual Operating Costs, dollars	Benefits
	Immediate Construction [a]	Construction by 1990 [b]	Total Construction		
(A) Secondary treatment at all plants and phosphorus removal	1.285	1.41	2.695	$5–6	Improved water quality for most tributaries and for Lake as a whole
(B) (A) plus advanced treatments at 67 plants	1.385	1.70	3.085	$7	Swimming and fishing increased to near full potential
(C) Advanced treatment at all plants	1.525	1.56	3.085	$10	Essentially the same as (B)
(D) (C) plus control of agriculture runoff and improved sewers	—	—	8.0+	—	An unspecified further improvement in water quality

Source: *Lake Erie Report*, Chapter 6, "The Cost of Pollution Control."
[a] Immediate construction-cost figures include an estimated 285 million dollars for industrial wastes in all programs. The remaining costs all apply to treatment of municipal wastes.
[b] Estimated on the basis of present-value calculations.

(2) For each performance level, the study examined only one alternative method. There is thus no particular reason to believe that the alternatives considered represent the lowest cost method of achieving that performance level. It can be seen from Table 2-2 that Program C has additional costs but no additional benefits beyond that of Program B. It is clear, therefore, that Program B is superior to Program C. Are there, however, other alternatives not examined in this study that would produce the same performance results as B at lower cost? The cost analyses being suggested are designed to answer this kind of question.

In considering this question there are a large number of alternatives that might be considered. First, there are a number of processes other than waste treatment, such as low flow augmentation and reoxygenation, that might be considered in relation to the tributaries. Second, there is the possibility of saving costs by making more effective use of the assimilative capacity of the Lake by changing the time and space patterns of waste discharge through effluent storage and redistribution. Third, there is the possibility of saving costs by taking advantage of economies of scale in the treatment process. Industrial and municipal wastes in a given area may be treated together at lower overall per-unit costs. And, possibly, savings can be realized by altering the uniform minimum treatment standard adopted by the FWQA. It follows from a well-known economic proposition that the maximum amount of waste treatment per dollar can be achieved only if the incremental (or marginal) costs of treatment are equal for all plants. The existence of economies of scale indicates that savings could, therefore, be realized by having larger communities treat wastes more intensively than smaller communities.

Merely listing these alternatives reveals, of course, that the task of finding low-cost alternatives is not easy. When one considers that the various approaches can be combined in different ways and to different extents, the number of available alternatives becomes greatly multiplied. Dealing with this level of complexity will require a systematic strategy. This study should, therefore, employ strategies that have been developed for dealing with this kind of situation in previous studies.[9] Essentially, the problem will be simplified by a sampling procedure. By use of the physical simulation models different alternatives can be related to performance levels. A set of fixed performance levels of interest can be selected. Different alternatives and tradeoffs between combinations of alternatives for each of the fixed performance levels may then be systematically sampled. By estimating the costs related to each of the sampled alternatives and alternative combinations, a general definition of the shape of the cost function can be developed.

Finally, on the basis of this function, low-cost alternatives can be determined for each of the different performance levels.

(3) The third information gap in the FWQA study pertains to the analysis of benefits. Although benefits are identified and described, they are not quantified, and they are not translatable into dollar terms so that they can be directly compared to costs. Even if Program B were the lowest cost method of bringing swimming and fishing opportunities in Lake Erie near to their potential, it is not clear that undertaking this program is necessarily in the public interest. In order for this to be so, the benefits from the swimming and fishing must be greater than the costs of providing them.

Recreation Benefits. Of all the different kinds of benefits related to the use of the Great Lakes, those related to recreational and aesthetic uses are by far the most difficult to measure. It is certainly understandable, therefore, why the FWQA did not provide these estimates. In fact, there are reasons for believing that these benefits, especially those relating to the more subtle aesthetic dimensions, are not entirely amenable to measurement. To the extent that this is true, the economic analyses are limited to the nevertheless highly useful role of showing the incremental costs of achieving incremental levels of water quality. With this information, public decision makers can at least know the minimum amount that additional improvements in water quality must be worth before the costs of producing them can be justified.

The Battelle program, however, seeks to accomplish considerably more than this. In the course of the last three years Battelle has conducted research which has been successful in advancing the state-of-the-art of estimating recreation benefits. A method for estimating benefits of outdoor recreation has been developed and tested. The method, it should be noted, is not designed to measure all aesthetic values, such as those that might arise from simply viewing or driving along a scenic shoreline. It is, however, ideally suited to measuring benefits that are associated with attendance at specific recreation sites, such as parks and beaches.

According to the FWQA study, this kind of recreation is indeed an important part of the total. Many beaches and resort areas have already been restricted, closed down, or abandoned because of water pollution. Figure 2-7 illustrates the large number of different sites that have been affected. The method developed by Battelle makes it possible to estimate the benefits that may be attributed to reopening these sites and the development of new sites that improved water quality of the Lake might make possible.

The method for estimating recreation benefits takes into account the interactions among the three components of all recreation systems: (1) the *people* who make decisions to recreate or not to recreate and to visit

38

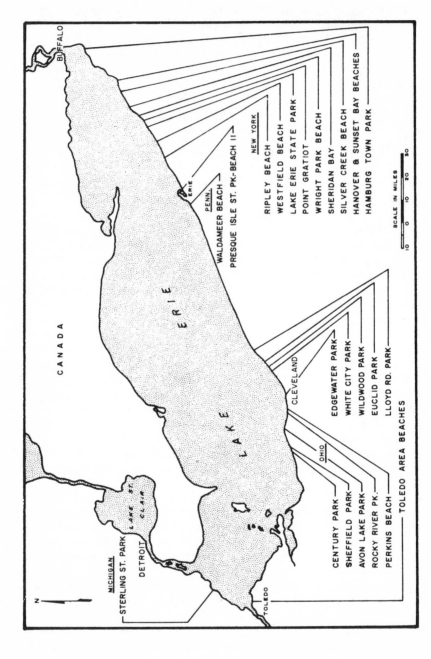

Figure 2-7. Polluted Beach Areas in Lake Erie (Source: *Lake Erie Report*, op. cit., p. 3)

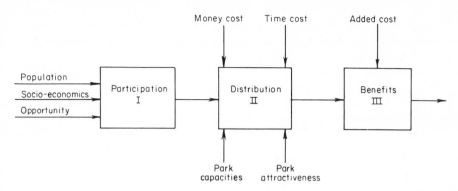

Figure 2-8. Three-stage Recreation Model

one park or another; (2) the *parks* that compete with one another for visitors; and (3) the *roads and highways* over which people travel to and from their recreation destinations. The estimation procedure involves the development of a three-stage model as shown in Figure 2-8. In the first stage, an estimate is made of the total amount of participation, that is, demand, for recreation in the entire area under consideration. In addition to the usual factors, such as the size of the population and its socio-economic makeup, this approach takes explicit account of the effect of changes in opportunity to recreate. Thus, an estimate can be made of the additional recreation that would be attributable to opening new sites or reopening old sites on the Lake. In the second stage, a model distributes the recreation participants among the various alternative recreation sites available. As indicated in Figure 2-8, this model takes explicit account of the capacities and relative attractiveness of the alternative sites as well as their relative accessibility to the participants. This model permits determination of to what extent attendance at new sites on the Lake will be at the expense of attendance at nearby competing sites not on the Lake. The final stage estimates the benefits that may be attributed to each site in the system of parks. This stage takes as input from Stage 2 the number of visitors at each park and estimates benefits on the basis of how much these visitors would be willing to pay. This stage is an extension and refinement of the so-called Clawson technique and imputes willingness to pay on the basis of out-of-pocket costs incurred by visitors in traveling to the parks. For the interested reader, Appendix E provides a detailed technical description of the method.

How Should Programs Be Financed

Besides determining their economic desirability, practical implementation of programs requires that some suitable means be found for their financing. Unfortunately, in the context of a common pool flow-resource system such as that represented by the Great Lakes, this requirement is particularly difficult to meet.

In the case of public goods, such as those of interest here, three basically different approaches to raising the necessary funds are conceivable. These are (1) voluntary contributions; (2) taxation; and (3) user charges. Each of these approaches has both advantages and disadvantages.

The voluntary contribution approach has the obvious advantage of entailing no coercion. Unfortunately, the approach has a major flaw—the free-rider problem. Under this approach some people would stand to benefit from the program but not pay their share of the costs. This inherent inequity would in turn discourage still others, who might ordinarily do so, from paying their share. In the end, this approach would no doubt lead to a woefully underfunded program.

Taxation. Taxation, despite its coercive nature, is frequently justified because it is an effective way of overcoming the free-rider problem. However, there are many different kinds of taxes and each different tax proposal has different implications as to who bears the costs. Unless the incidence of the tax being used corresponds to the incidence of the benefits being generated, the taxation approach also leads to problems. Those who are overtaxed, that is, pay more than they benefit, will tend to keep the program underfunded. To help public decision makers avoid this kind of problem, the proposed economic analysis will determine the probable incidence of alternative tax configurations that might be used for program funding.

The problems in using taxation as a method of raising funds can be aptly illustrated from the FWQA study of Lake Erie. Figure 2-9 shows the areas that are primarily responsible for pollution of the Lake. Corresponding to that, Figure 2-10 shows how the immediate construction costs of implementing the recommended program are distributed over different areas of the Lakes. Comparison of these figures with Figure 2-7 showing the distribution of recreation sites that would be affected by cleaner Lake water is revealing. It can be seen that there is a very poor correspondence between areas that must treat their waste discharge and areas (in the vicinity of the affected beaches) that would probably capture most of the benefits. Most significantly it can be seen that the Detroit-Southeast Michigan area, under local financing, would have to bear nearly 50 percent of the total costs and yet, with no affected beaches in the vicinity, probably receive very little of the benefits.

Even if analysis of benefits shows that the overall program proposed by the FWQA is economically desirable, it is hard to imagine responsible public officials in southeastern Michigan willingly using their local tax funds to finance it. In general, wherever the costs that must be incurred

41

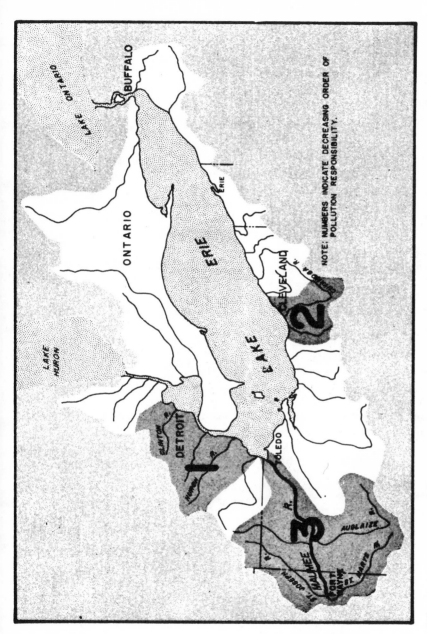

Figure 2-9. Areas of Primary Responsibility for Pollution of Lake Erie (Source: *Lake Erie Report*, op. cit., p. 4)

by local areas exceed the benefits they can capture, the same problem can be expected to occur. The net result of relying on locally raised tax funds will be substantially less investment in the program than from an overall standpoint is economically desirable.

Under these circumstances, local parties who stand to benefit by the program frequently turn to higher levels of government for funds. This ploy is sometimes very successful. If there are enough beneficiaries and if they are politically strong enough in the higher level organization, whether it be state or federal, a substantial amount of the funding may be obtained in this way. It is not at all clear, however, that this approach will be successful. And despite its higher chance for success, it is not clear that this approach to financing is any more equitable than the local taxation alternative.

In general, to the extent that the government agency involved has jurisdictional boundaries which are much larger than the benefit receiving area, problems will exist. And, in the case where boundaries are too small, there is likely to be inaction or underinvestment because part of the population may have to share the costs of actions from which they do not benefit. Under this circumstance the nonbenefited population may either inhibit effective action or demand costly side payments for cooperation.

User Charges. The third approach to raising funds, user charges, is particularly attractive because it avoids both the problems of the free rider and the overtaxed nonbeneficiary. Despite these obvious advantages, user charges are infrequently used to provide funds for public services because of a host of associated difficulties. In some cases—for example, the provision of urban highway transportation—the costs of collecting fees are prohibitive. In other cases, the primary consumers are not the main beneficiaries. A good example is the county jail. In still other cases—for example clean air—there is no way of denying use of the goods to those who do not pay. A particularly nice feature of most of the water-related goods and services of interest here is that they are, in contrast to the preceding examples, relatively amenable to the user charge approach. This would be true, for example, of water supply, waste disposal, hydroelectric power, navigation, and recreation.

In addition to these obvious advantages, the user charge approach has other, somewhat more subtle advantages. Through user charges it may be possible to reduce the total costs of the program. For example, the FWQA in its study estimates that the recommended construction for treating industrial wastes would cost about 285 million dollars. But, it concedes that this is an extremely rough estimate because "costs for industrial waste discharge are difficult to determine due to the many processes involved with such a diversity of industries located within the Lake Erie Basin." [10] Because of the diversity, it is clear that the costs of re-

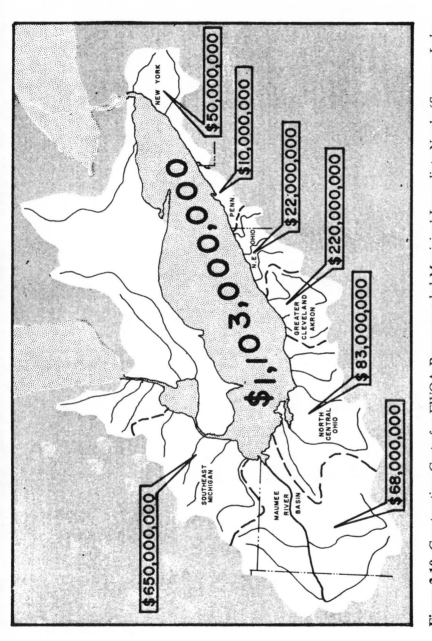

Figure 2.10. Construction Costs for FWQA Recommended Municipal Immediate Needs (Source: *Lake Erie Report*, op. cit., p. 85)

ducing waste discharge will vary significantly among industries and even among firms in the same industry. A low-cost method of treating a given amount of waste requires that the incremental cost of treating the last unit of waste incurred by all firms be equal. This can occur only if different firms treat at different levels. By levying a user charge, in contrast to a user standard, each firm in pursuing its own self-interest will treat up to the point where its incremental treatment cost equals the user charge. Beyond that point, the firm will find it cheaper to pay the user charge. Since all firms in a given area will face the same user charge, they will all produce to the point where their incremental costs are equal. This is precisely the lowest cost solution.

In addition to user charges for pollution, it may be desirable to place user charges on recreationists. One of the important advantages of the Battelle method of estimating recreation benefits is that it provides information on what people are willing to pay for these opportunities. It would thus be possible to estimate the amount of revenues that may be raised under various assumed user charge schemes. It may be that revenues raised in this way could more than pay for the required pollution control program and would preclude the need for raising additional taxes.

In general, a critical question that must be answered, if the user charge approach is to be implemented successfully, is what price should be charged. Unlike his counterpart in private industry, a public official may not want to charge a price designed to maximize net revenues, since, if the user charges are too high, many prospective users may be driven away, and the amount of benefits realized by the public thereby reduced. On the other hand, if user charges are too low, the agency may not obtain enough revenues to adequately fund the program. In short, user charges must be carefully set in order to steer a middle course between not enough public benefits, on the one hand, and not enough net revenues on the other. An important part of the economic analyses is, therefore, aimed at determining the consequences of alternative user charge policies.

Integration of Tasks

It should be stressed that the analyses envisioned here represent a coherent and integrated sequence of tasks. This is illustrated in the flow diagram in Figure 2-11.

The analyses begin with a search for and an identification of alternatives. This can be done in close consultation with technological experts. Next, those alternatives are compared and evaluated through application of cost and benefit analyses. Next, estimates can be made of how the benefits of the more promising programs are distributed. The distribution of benefits is then compared with the distribution of costs under various financing schemes. Finally, using the information on cost and benefit

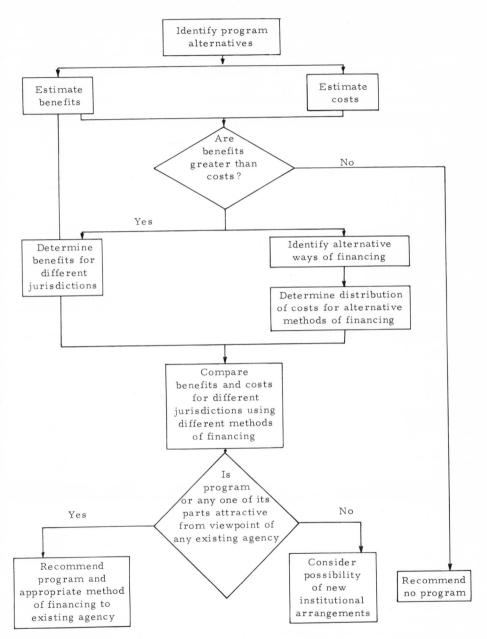

Figure 2-11. Logical Flow of Tasks

distribution, judgment can be made regarding the desirability of different programs from the standpoint of different existing public agencies.

To the extent that desirable programs are not attractive to existing agencies, the possibilities of establishing new institutional arrangements will be considered. The approach to the analyses is described in the subsequent section on institutional analyses.

Institutional Analyses

**S. E. Goldston, M. H. Karr, Vincent and
Elinor Ostrom** *

Institutional problems relative to water and related land resources development and management are clearly defined by the Federal Council for Science and Technology in its July 1968, report on needed research, titled "Water Resources Policy and Political Institutions." The greatest need is in developing and applying methods that will realistically measure the performance of institutions in order to identify ". . . those policies and institutional arrangements which are conducive to sound water management." The Council recommends extensive use of case studies or postaudit techniques in order to evaluate the several important aspects of institutional arrangements.

The importance of this is verified by the Office of Water Resources Research in its priority listing of research projects published in the June 23, 1969, issue of *Commerce Business Daily*. Under the heading, "Water Resources Policy and Political Institutions," OWRR states, "Understanding of policy and institutional problems is indispensable to sound water resources management by both the publc and private sectors of the Nation."

There is no question that an assessment of the institutional problems arising from the development of common pool, flow-resource systems is essential for an understanding of the general dynamics affecting the development of the Great Lakes-St. Lawrence River System. The Great Lakes represents a classic example of a common pool resource offering the possibility of many joint and alternative benefits if users can avoid some of the typical dynamics engendered by the very nature of the resource system. Some inherent difficulties of organizing any relatively efficient and equitable set of institutions for managing common pool resources are outlined in Appendix F, "A Political Theory for Institutional Analysis." This appendix summarizes a theory which offers promise in analyzing political calculations relevant to decision making in common pool water-resource situations.

Theoretical Basis for Analysis

A number of general propositions or theorems about the strategic behavior of individuals utilizing a common pool resource can be derived from the abovementioned theory, as summarized below.

---

* Professors of Political Science, Indiana University.

Proposition 1. From the economic calculus of decision making based upon evaluation of personal costs and benefits, individuals utilizing a scarce common pool resource without public intervention will be led to make decisions which produce social costs for others. They will tend to overinvest in facilities concerned with their own private use and under-invest in projects to produce joint benefits for a community of users.

Proposition 2. Intense competition for the utilization of the resource will lead individual users to adopt any or all of the following patterns of conduct: (a) Concealing information about resource utilization and the potential social costs for others; (b) ignoring the adverse effects on the use of the resource; and following a hold-out strategy when projects of joint benefit are proposed.

Proposition 3. Without collective action, the predominant outcome of competitive use of a scarce common pool resource will be eventual domi-nation by one use or user (or one group of compatible uses) resulting in less of opportunities for beneficial use by others. The dominant use or set of uses will tend to be the one that produces the largest accrued social cost to the total community of prior and potential users.

Proposition 4. Averting such competitive costs or gaining the benefits of investment in common facilities are potential social benefits that indi-viduals will attempt to capture in diverse ways such as appealing to a public agency having appropriate boundaries and range of authority for action in their joint interest.

Proposition 5. A public agency with boundaries smaller than the prob-lem to be solved would tend to require the individuals it represents to pay to reduce the social costs of their actions while leaving others free to generate social costs having adverse effects upon those within its jurisdic-tion—or to pay for the construction of projects of benefit not only to those it represents but to others beyond those boundaries who thereby re-ceive free benefits without bearing the costs of improvement.

Proposition 6. If a public agency exists with boundaries considerably larger than the problem to be solved, extraneous populations may share the cost of actions from which they do not benefit and may demand costly side payments for cooperation in any joint effort.

Proposition 7. The existence of a potential social benefit and the lack of an appropriate existing public agency may lead individuals to attempt to constitute a new collective or public enterprise, the nature and social cost of which would be dependent upon the decision rules considered.

Proposition 8. A decision rule which allows only a small proportion of those affected by a public jurisdiction to make decisions binding on all others tends to impose high deprivation costs on those who disagree with the adopted policies, while, in contrast, a decision rule which requires a large proportion of the affected individuals to agree prior to action tends to impose high costs in the time, money, and effort spent in decision making.

Proposition 9. If there is a range of decision rules which produces internal decision-making costs less than the potential benefits to be derived from collective action, a political surplus exists, which results in a net benefit to be gained from organizing a public enterprise.

Proposition 10. Since the boundary of the problem to be solved and the range of decision-making costs can vary significantly for different types of collective action, individuals may be motivated to devise separate enterprises to provide different types of joint benefits.

Proposition 11. The boundaries of public decision-making arrangements capable of dealing with common pool problems at one time may not be sufficient to handle such problems at a later time, since there cannot be a single, permanent solution to resource management problems.

Proposition 12. Systematic biasing of information by public entrepreneurs may lead individuals at an early juncture to establish enterprises with decision rules which impose a high level of deprivation costs on others.

Proposition 13. Technological innovation may lead, on the one hand, to the production of new spillover costs that previous institutional arrangements did not anticipate or, on the other hand, to the production of new potential social benefits not previously available.

Proposition 14. Individuals attempting to manage and utilize a common pool resource can make more optimal decisions if there is an independent third party who can provide unbiased information to all affected parties and will tend to seek the optimum solution if some form of pricing or taxing is utilized to reflect the opportunity costs involved.

Collectively, the propositions lead to the conclusions that sound management of common pool resources requires (a) a mix of large and small-scale public and private agencies; (b) accurate information available to all affected parties provided by someone not involved in production activities related to the common pool; and (c) some form of user charges (pricing, taxing arrangements, or other technique) which induces individuals to take the social costs of their actions into account in the decision-making process.

Authoritative Structure

The above propositions also help to provide an explanation as to how and why the institutional patterns of the Great Lakes evolved to their present form and provide an outline for evaluation of the current structure which could lead to recommendations for needed institutional reforms. The existing structure of governmental authority defines the essential terms and conditions for establishing the political feasibility of any program of action. Since governmental jurisdiction and the exercise of governmental decision-making capabilities significantly affect the opportunities for water resource management in the Great Lakes system, the characteristics of the different political regimes bearing upon the Great Lakes Basin need to be well understood prior to any analysis of its water-resource problems.

General Structure. The international boundary between the United States and Canada is defined in relation to the water course of the Great Lakes-St. Lawrence River system from a point where the 45th parallel intersects the St. Lawrence River near St. Regis, New York, and Cornwall, Ontario, westward through Lakes Ontario, Erie, Huron, and to the western shore of Lake Superior. Only Lake Michigan is wholly within the boundaries of the United States. Since Lake Michigan and Lake Huron constitute a single pool of water, many aspects of Lake Michigan's development are highly interdependent with those of Lake Huron and the other lakes lower in the system.

Because of the international character, no one governmental jurisdiction with overall authority exists in the Great Lakes Basin. Problems of an international character are resolved by mutual agreement of the respective governments involved or by reference to decision-making mechanisms that are established by these governments to act on their behalf. An International Joint Commission was established by the Boundary Waters Treaty of 1909 to perform certain consultative, investigatory, recommendatory, and adjudicatory functions associated with all boundary waters affecting the United States and Canada and is not limited to the Great Lakes-St. Lawrence system. Many other joint American-Canadian arrangements exist regarding hydroelectric power production, navigation, fisheries, and the construction and operation of bridges across boundary waters.

Both the United States and Canada have political constitutions which provide for a complex division of authority among many different units of government within each nation and for separate decision structures within each unit of government. Neither political system involves the assignment of sovereign prerogative over all affairs of government to a single political regime. Instead, these two North American countries are composed of a system of political regimes operating within a federal system.

The crude similarities between these two constitutional systems are greatly complicated by quite different assignments of authority within and among the different units of government in the United States and Canada. The constitutional formula in the United States, for example, clearly recognizes the exclusive and controlling interests of the national government in international affairs. The Canadian constitution, by contrast, is much more ambiguous about the exclusive authority of the national government in those international matters that impinge upon the jurisdiction of the provinces.

Canadian provinces exercise a much more extensive authority over the management of land and water resources than is exercised by American states. In turn, municipalities and other local units of government in the United States may have a great measure of constitutional prerogative in defining the terms and conditions of their self-government as formulated in home-rule charters. While eight American states border the Great Lakes, only one Canadian province, Ontario, occupies the entire expanse of the Canadian territory bordering the Great Lakes. Political prerogatives of the numerous American cities along the Great Lakes vary significantly from each other and from metropolitan Toronto.

The constitution of authority within each unit of government varies radically between the United States and Canada. Canada adheres more closely to the formula of the British parliamentary system in defining the structure of authority among the various decision structures comprising a particular unit of government. Under that formula, the doctrine of parliamentary supremacy vests with the legislature ultimate authority over all matters of public policy within the competence of a particular unit of government. It also places control over both legislative and executive leadership in a cabinet formed by the majority party or coalition of parties in the legislature. The force of legislative supremacy is reflected in the fact that a provincial constitution in Canada is no more than a law passed by a provincial legislature. The Canadian judiciary is a federal or national judiciary without a separate system of provincial courts.

The United States, by contrast, has relied upon a doctrine of separation of powers in the assignment of authority within each major unit of government. Prerogatives of constitutional decision making are formulated so that either an extraordinary majority vote or a general referendum is required to affirm changes in the basic decision rules contained within a constitution. The exercise of governmental prerogative is limited by constitutional proscription. Courts of law have general competence to rule upon the validity of governmental action. Legislative bodies are independently elected so as to represent different sets of constituencies. The viability of public action depends upon affirmative decisions in several different decision structures, each of which is capable of exercising a veto by refusing to act.

Specific Institutional Structure. Over the course of United States and Canadian history, large numbers of specific institutional settlements regarding use and development of water resources for various purposes have been reached by people residing in the Great Lakes Basin. These settlements represent the result of political investments in human organization. The current political structure can be conceptualized as the institutional capital which provides a base for any further advances. Existing arrangements must be taken into account in building new forms of organization and in constituting new patterns of public enterprise. Since most studies of institutional arrangements focus on one or, at best, a limited number of governmental instrumentalities in relationship to a complex resource system, little is known about the patterns of interaction between and among public and private enterprises in the Great Lakes system. Only conjectures about the operation of the aggregate political structure of the Great Lakes Region can be provided at this point. An important research need is to gain insight about these patterns of interaction.

From the framework of concurrent regimes which form the basis of the political constitutions in both the United States and Canada, it is evident that institutional structures bearing upon the Great Lakes have been organized at various levels: (1) individual action and voluntary associations; (2) local governmental organization; (3) state and provincial government organization; (4) federal governmental organization; and (5) international organizations such as the International Joint Commission.

Particular patterns of water utilization also have led to concurrent patterns of organization among different levels of political organization. Thus, problems of navigation involve international, federal, state, and provincial law as well as local ordinances. Such developments also involve the provision of dock and harbor facilities by state and local agencies, maintenance of navigation channels, operation of navigational locks, and the construction of canals by agencies at the federal and international levels. Other functions, such as the provision of water for municipal and industrial purposes, generally occur only at the private and local governmental levels, subject to regulation by authorities at the state, provincial, and federal levels.

Any long-term effort to understand the patterns of water resource development of the Great Lakes will require a general inventory of these institutional arrangements, with special attention to patterns of vertical and horizontal interdependencies among agencies. It can be anticipated that the vertical relationships will involve interdependencies and exchanges that are somewhat analogous to those within an industry where production, wholesaling, and retailing functions may become differentiated from one another. Governmental instrumentalities may function as the producers of services that are sold at a wholesale rate to other public jurisdictions which, in turn, sell related services to consumers.

Assuming that governmental agencies associated with the provision of diverse goods and services in the Great Lakes area are members of water-related industries makes it possible to bring order to the complex relationships between and among the large number of jurisdictions involved. For example, the St. Lawrence Seaway Authority of Canada and the St. Lawrence Development Corporation of the United States would appear to be among the large-scale producers of navigation services within the Great Lakes system. There would also appear to be a great deal of independence of action encouraged at the local levels in the provision of dock and harbor facilities to supplement the more general facilities of the Seaway and to serve the navigational and commercial interests of local communities.

Various patterns of water use, such as municipal water supplies, sewerage and waste disposal, fisheries, power production, and recreation, can be viewed in terms of the degree of vertical differentiation that has occurred in the development of the Great Lakes water-related economy. The operation of relatively large-scale public enterprises for purposes of water quality management in one or more of the Lakes, or for purposes of fisheries development, may involve entrepreneurial opportunities beyond those developed in other water resource-management systems.

The terms of trade among different public enterprises involve fiscal transfers from one jurisdiction to another. In some cases, these have the characteristics of a pricing mechanism involving direct payment for services rendered. In other cases, a nomenclature of grants in aid may partially obscure what is essentially a *quid pro quo* where a larger jurisdiction buys the production of a service supplied by smaller jurisdictions. Also involved are exchanges of information, exchanges of services in kind, and exchanges of political support in the maintenance of voting coalitions. These various terms of trade, and the patterns of organization for sustaining such relationships between and among agencies, must be carefully examined in any evaluation of the performance of water service industries in the Great Lakes economy.

Because of the differences in the structuring of decision-making capabilities within each unit of government, marked differences exist between the United States and Canada in the relative industrial configurations existing among water use and development agencies functioning within the Great Lakes system. Canadian arrangements will tend to be dominated by two different centers of authority—at Ottawa and Toronto. United States agencies will represent substantial dispersion of operating responsibility among local and states agencies and among the several federal agencies interested in water resource development. These differences provide opportunities to assess different institutional arrangements on a comparative basis.

Certain predictable biases will be introduced into the decision-making processes occurring at the international level. It would be expected that Canadian negotiating teams would include strong representation of provincial as well as federal authorities. Each would occupy strong and potentially independent bargaining positions based upon quite different sets of constituency interests. Each could exercise an ultimate veto position, and any negotiated settlement must take into account the bargaining parameters of both.

By contrast, it is likely that United States negotiating teams would be composed exclusively of federal authorities, and would take into account primarily those interests which involve entrepreneurial opportunities affecting the operation of federal agencies. For example, interests in navigation, qualified by the Corps of Engineers' traditional aversion to user fees, would be strongly represented, while interests in the use of the Great Lakes for fisheries development and recreational purposes would be more weakly represented. The strategic influence of chairmen and leading members of powerful committees in Congress is apt to introduce an extraneous factor affecting the political viability of any international undertaking upon the Great Lakes and requiring collateral negotiation of some political trade off. Joint development of the St. Lawrence Seaway, for example, was delayed by protracted negotiations and by prolonged deliberation in the U.S. Congress, where coastal shipping and railroad interests viewed the Seaway as unwelcome competition. Joint development was finally authorized only after Canada indicated a willingness and a capability to develop an all-Canadian alternative.

Research Needs

An overview of the general and specific structure of authority related to the management of the water resources of the Great Lakes Basin shows that a great deal of effort has been invested in attempts to solve a number of important resource management problems. However, there are indications that existing institutional arrangements are, in part, deficient. Perhaps the most significant indicator is the gradually decreasing quality levels in parts of the Lakes, particularly Lake Erie, requiring initiation of both preventative and restorative measures related to the many factors that contribute to the quality degradation that adversely affects many users.

If institutional development is to be considered as a feasible approach to water management, the important question then becomes: How would one formulate an analysis for the Great Lakes Basin that would provide a sound

basis for assessing existing institutions and for identifying desirable directions for the development or modification of institutional arrangements?

Needed research on institutional factors is a logical consequence of the
implications from the theoretical propositions presented in that (1) reasonable individuals rationally pursuing their own self-interest cannot be
expected to voluntarily arrive at a set of optimal institutional arrangements; and (2) the characteristics of an optimal institutional arrangement
will depend upon the particular circumstances, so that viability to meet
changing conditions is a desired characteristic.

For these reasons, meaningful institutional analysis could play a catalytic
role in the development process in the Great Lakes Basin. In light of the
nonautomatic nature of institutional development, applied research may
fruitfully be devoted to an analysis of particular problem situations, such
as pollution in Lake Erie. In this context, the research could identify the
existence and probable magnitude of potential social benefits that are not
currently being captured by existing institutions, and then determine
whether and how they might be captured through modification of existing
public enterprises, through the formation of new enterprises, or by some
combination of these approaches.

Such problem-focused research is most suitable in cases where the
potential benefits to be captured are amenable to measurement. At this
point, the extent to which the political surplus can actually be measured is
not clear. The theory indicates that it is precisely where the potential
benefits are most difficult to measure that political surplus is most likely to
remain untapped. This is because of the inherent informational bias, in
such circumstances, toward underestimating the value of net benefits of
collective action relative to opportunity and deprivation costs.

In circumstances where accurate measurement is not feasible, institu-
tional-focused rather than problem-focused research would be useful.
Since the theory indicates the importance of viability, research should be
directed toward determining to what extent this characteristic is actually
achieved. An analytical description of the existing Great Lakes institutional
arrangements should be made and compared with common resource pool
institutions in operation elsewhere. In this way, new institutional techniques
and arrangements could be identified that would provide individuals in
the Great Lakes area with more options and more abilities to realize the
potential benefits of collective action. An institution-focused approach
would constitute a mutually reinforcing combination with the problem-
focused approach.

Such a research program would, at the same time, appreciably strengthen
the basic theoretical tools and methodologies for dealing with institutional
problems and for providing a basis for decision making. In effect, the
usefulness and validity of the theoretical concepts would be demonstrated
early in the research program. This interaction between theory and application will facilitate the sharpening, extension, revision, and overall strength-

ening of sociopolitical theory, and the results would have nationwide and international application.

Scope of the Program

An evaluation of the Lake Erie situation could serve as an initial demonstration of research capabilities in institutional analysis. This study would be used to develop longer term capabilities for undertaking other analyses of significance in the Great Lakes Basin, with potential application to institutional problems in other regions of the United States and Canada.

The program would involve three interrelated components which would be developed concurrently:

(1) Assessment of institutional arrangements for water resources development in several large urban complexes tributary to Lake Erie, including the Detroit-Windsor, Toledo, Cleveland, and Buffalo areas, and Canadian lakeshore communities on the north shore.

(2) Design of institutional arrangements relevant to the development and operation of a large-scale water quality management program for Lake Erie as a whole. This would require an assessment of various feasibility criteria including technical, economic, financial, legal, and political considerations. It would also encompass a projection of the consequences of introducing or not introducing the designed arrangements in relation to (a) water quality in Lake Erie; and (b) changes in the conduct and performance of existing institutional facilities.

(3) An evaluation of the theory and methods of institutional analysis.

All three components taken together provide a basis for formulating workable solutions to particular institutional arrangements in water resource development. By a postaudit of experience, in light of results anticipated in design formulations, the basic theory used in institutional analysis can be tested and modified where necessary.

Elements of the Program

Component 1. Assessment of Institutional Arrangements for Lake Erie. Among all of the Great Lakes, some of the most critical problems in water quality control which impinge upon various patterns of use are to be found in Lake Erie. These problems have been well documented by FWQA.

Lake Erie receives a relatively large pollution load from the Detroit-Windsor metropolitan area, which is substantially added to by the Ohio cities along its south shore. The waste discharge provides an abundant supply of nutrients which, together with warmer temperatures afforded by the shallowness of the lake, contribute to excessive algal growths which, in turn, create many problems associated with such things as municipal and industrial water supply, fishlife, and recreation. In short, the dynamics of the common pool problems may lead to such serious deterioration in the water quality of the Lake that much of its utility for several purposes could be lost.

This, then, is a critical juncture for undertaking a research program designed to assess the institutional arrangements for various forms of water resource use and development among different types of tributary communities in the Lake Erie Basin. Such an assessment would serve two purposes. First, it would provide an opportunity to make a comparative analysis of significantly different institutional arrangements in proximity to Lake Erie. Second, it would provide an inventory of existing institutional arrangements which may be viewed as a part of the political capital that is available for dealing with water quality problems of the Lake.

Institutional arrangements for the use and development of water resources in five different tributary communities should be examined in this component of the Lake Erie demonstration study: (1) the Detroit-Windsor area, (2) the Toledo area, (3) the Cleveland area, (4) the Buffalo area, and (5) the Canadian lakeshore communities along the north shore of Lake Erie. Two of these, the Detroit-Windsor and Cleveland areas, are among the ten largest metropolitan areas in North American. The Toledo and Cleveland areas are located in one state and comparably situated in relation to Lake Erie and, therefore, constitute a high degree of comparability in problems of water use and development requiring similar types of institutional solutions. Deviations in the particular patterns of institutional arrangements between these two communities, thus, would provide for a comparative assessment of the performances inherent in different institutional arrangements within tributary communities.

The Detroit-Windsor metropolitan area in many ways is a single metropolitan community transcending an international boundary. Thus, the particular institutional arrangements existing on the United States and Canadian sides of the border would reflect the political calculations inherent in the opportunities and limitations afforded by two fundamentally different political regimes with no overlapping jurisdiction. The Detroit-Windsor area is situated in relation to the Lake Erie Basin, in a position enabling it to easily segregate patterns of water use. Uses requiring high-quality water can be located upstream along Lake St. Clair and the St. Clair River. Users able to tolerate lower standards of water quality, and those having a detrimental effect on water quality, generally prime industrial users, can be placed downstream along the Detroit River, where effluent discharges would pass directly into the Lake Erie water pool. However, the relatively high decision-making costs in this bination community resulting from dependency upon fundamentally different political regimes can have an adverse effect upon the net performance of water-related institutions providing water services for the Detroit-Windsor metropolitan community.

The Buffalo metropolitan area represents the obverse of the Detroit situation in relation to the Lake Erie pool. Buffalo is in a situation where it can spill wastes downstream into the Niagara River and the Lake Ontario Basin. However, water quality problems may not permit advantage to be taken of segregating water use patterns.

Both Toledo and Cleveland have minimal opportunities for segregating water use patterns in relation to the Lake Erie pool. As a consequence, it would be expected that the water agencies in these two metropolitan communities would take a greater account of the external costs that each agency or set of agencies will have upon one another. Consequently, there is probably a higher level of sophistication in coordination between these two tributary communities and a higher level of performance by their water agencies.

The Canadian lakeshore communities are smaller and more dispersed in their location along the north shore. Under these circumstances, there probably is less sophistication in the development of their institutional arrangements for water-related activities.

With the possible exception of the Canadian lakeshore communities, elaborate institutional arrangements can be expected, somewhat analogous to an industry structure, to have developed in each of the tributary communities to be studied, so that in essence, a joint-product industry is being dealt with. Therefore, careful attention must be given to the interdependencies and terms of trade between enterprises devoted to competing uses. This would include the horizontal relationship which affects each agency's opportunities for development while providing different water services to much the same community of users. Interdependencies may be such that demand for water for different uses can create mutually advantageous terms of trade. For example, a municipality which has to bear the costs of its waste discharges as an impairment of its own recreational areas and source of water supply could be led to reclaim and reuse its waste waters for the benefit of its own joint use. Or, if a large-scale water quality management enterprise were to establish a pricing schedule for waste discharges and for the use of quality controlled water from the Lake as opportunity costs, added incentives would be created to encourage local water agencies to reclaim and recycle water where they could advantageously do so.

Studies undertaken on the institutional arrangements should be organized in relation to comparable analytical variables and performance criteria in accordance with the following outline:

I. Structure
    A. Resource system—supply
    B. Population and patterns of economic development—demand
    C. Water law and the general structure of political authority

D. Water-related enterprises and institutional arrangements
   1. Number and variety of public and private agencies
   2. Territorial jurisdiction and service areas
   3. Functional range of authority for water use and development (including constraints upon functions of a water service agency)
   4. Physical plant and service facilities
   5. External effects
   6. Fiscal arrangements
      a. Investment policies and practices
      b. Pricing policies and practices
      c. Taxing policies and practices
      d. Other fiscal policies and practices relating to fiscal transfers, grants in aid, and so on.
   7. Jurisdictional authority and regulatory conditions
E. Patterns of vertical differentiation
F. Patterns of horizontal differentiation

II. Conduct
A. Conflict—case studies including examination of
   1. The issues involved
   2. The course of the conflict
   3. How resolution, if any, was reached
   4. How the resolution affected the terms and conditions of accommodation among the competing agencies
   5. The continuing arrangement for various agencies to serve each other's operational conditions and requirements as the consequence of conflict resolution
B. Coordination
   1. Specialization and coordination (including reference to various patterns of exchange and terms of trade)
   2. Coordination through the action of political regimes
   3. Coordination through litigation in equity proceedings
   4. Coordination through voluntary associations
      a. Associations relating to vertical structures
      b. Associations relating to horizontal structures
C. Findings
   1. Dynamics of competitive rivalry and cooperative teamwork
   2. Conditions that bound and sustain such dynamics among the various water resource institutions

III. Performance Evaluation
A. Net effect upon water use, quantity, and quality
B. Relative efficiency
C. Allocational effects of pricing, taxing, rationing, and production policies
D. Relative equities

Component 2. Design and Feasibility Study of Institutional Arrangements for a Large-Scale Water Quality Management Program. Component 2 would comprise an assessment feasibility of an institutional arrangement to manage the quality of the Lake as a common resource. Such an effort would, in turn, depend upon an assessment of technical problems of water quality control as well as the institutional problems of meeting the various conditions necessary for the creation of a public enterprise capable of operating a water quality control program. Therefore, both engineering and institutional analyses would be necessary.

The design and feasibility study would first require an assessment of the aggregate water quality problem of Lake Erie, with consideration of alternative plans of action involving different control measures. This would be followed by an estimation of the potential social net benefits or deficits to be derived from implementation of alternative control measures using benefit-cost analysis in considering economic feasibility.

After the magnitude of the technical and economic components has been calculated, distribution of benefits which can be expected to flow from different control measures can be assessed through examination of financial feasibility. This would involve exploring the possibility of using various forms of pricing mechanisms such as user charges, different forms of taxation including so-called yield or severance taxes which might be imposed as a condition of use, and fiscal transfers which might also be associated with user charges, yield or severance taxes, or grants in aid schemes that transfer payments from large to smaller jurisdictions as an incentive for the latter to alter their production schedule to more closely approximate the demands of the larger community of users.

Once the assessments of technical, economic, and financial feasibility of alternative plans of action have been made, consideration can then be given to the legal feasibility of different components that appear to offer the most promising prospects for desirable management of the water quality of the Lake Erie system. This would identify legal conditions that would have to be met in order to implement the specific components of an action program.

Finally, political parameters can be considered to identify decision rules and conditions needed to sustain affirmative decisions in relation to each affected political regime. Decisions affecting the authorization of any such program as well as decisions affecting its continued operational viability can both be considered.

These several feasibility studies would provide the basis for an optimal program that integrates technical, economic, financial, legal, and political considerations into an aggregate cost calculus. The goal of this research component, then, would be to articulate the design for institutional arrangements that would approach optimal results and to identify the consequences of implementing alternative arrangements so the public would have a realistic choice.

Component 3. Evaluation of the Theory and Methodology. Problems bearing upon the use of different institutional arrangements for water resource development have been the subject of persistent debate and controversy for several decades. In more recent years, the debate has shifted to inquiries about the appropriateness of different forms of institutional arrangements. A recent report of the Federal Council for Science and Technology indicates the relative importance of institutional considerations by observing:

It is quite conceivable that the enactment of one piece of . . . legislation . . . could have more impact on the nature and extent of future water management than any single scientific gain of the next ten years.

A realistic method of measuring the performance of various institutional arrangements is one of the most pressing problems in water resource development. But, concern has not been matched by analytical capabilities, outside of the private sector where market dynamics permit adjustments to changing conditions of supply and demand.

The critical importance of asking the right questions, if reasonably good answers are expected in relation to difficult problems, dictates that a high priority be given to extension of current work in the theory and method of institutional analysis. This is needed in order to provide scientific developments in institutional analysis technology that may be used both in guiding research into problems of institutional arrangements and in developing political solutions based upon such analysis.

Recent developments in political theory which are reflected in Appendix F, "A Political Theory for Institutional Analysis," indicate some of the strategic calculations affecting decision making in relation to the development of water as a common pool flow resource.

These considerations need to be carried substantially further to a form that is applicable to the configuration of institutional arrangements providing water services in particular communities. The theoretical analysis should permit a reasonably accurate assessment of the capabilities and limitations inherent in the solutions attained by any particular community of water service users.

The use of this theory depends upon the formulation of indicators which can be used to measure aggregate benefits and costs without being limited to those which can be transposed into monetary values. Furthermore, these indicators need to be expressed in a form which can be characterized as a net anticipated surplus or deficit to be derived from any plan of operation. The suggested analysis, then, would involve an assessment of different forms of decision-making costs required to establish the political feasibility of any particular program of action. From this, the relative efficiency of different forms of institutional arrangement could be established to provide a method for assessing performance. Another method for assessing performance would be to consider the relative equity attained in the distribution of benefits and detriments among those affected by any given action program.

It is believed, on the basis of Battelle's analysis of institutional arrangements for Great Lakes water management, that extension and application of the common pool resource theory offers considerable promise in eventual institutional innovation. Preliminary examination of present arrangements confirms Battelle's belief in the descriptive accuracy of the theory as developed to date. The predictions of institutional arrangements derived from the common pool resource theory appear to be highly consistent with what has actually occurred in the historical development of Lake Erie.

Component 3, then, would be considered as a deliberate effort to extend the frontiers of theory and its validation in institutional analysis. It would be used to contribute to the design and formulation of the studies undertaken in Components 1 and 2 and would, in turn, draw upon the experiences gained in the research and analysis sustained in Components 1 and 2. This would represent an important extension of the state-of-the-art that would have application to institutional analysis under a variety of conditions and circumstances extending far beyond the Great Lakes Basin.

The International Great Lakes Center

R. T. Jaske, C. J. Touhill, I. L. Whitman

The administrative mechanism for the study program and the means needed to bring about the desired evolution in resource management concepts are difficult to perceive at this time. Having devoted considerable thought to this aspect, Battelle tentatively is suggesting the establishment of an International Great Lakes Center for Human Affairs and Technology.

It is expected that the Center and its programs might be the catalyst in the expected evolution of resource programs and policies. One process that must occur during this evolution would be greater interaction between resource planners and users. The program is intended to lay the groundwork for this process, as well as to advance the state of the art of technological analysis of water systems.

It would be premature at this time to specify organizational detail for the Center in anything but a cursory description, because its process of development would have to be evolutionary. However, it is possible to indicate some ideas on composition, activities, and means of support.

Center Composition

The operating components of the Center would include a number of interdependent institutes with specific functions and authority, primarily responsible for implementing the proposed program. These would be the major organs for achieving the necessary interactions between the public, the technological innovators, and the governmental and private institutions charged with the eventual task of making management decisions. The components of the Center and their functions are shown in Figure 2-12.

Institute for Human Affairs. The Institute for Human Affairs would be the primary link in the Great Lakes Center between technology and the humanities. Its purpose would be to perform and sponsor analyses of political, economic, and social behavior to enable evaluation of the impact of technological developments on man. This Institute would act as a so-called third party in its judgment on the desirability of potential impacts of resource development and management procedures on the Lakes and the Basin. This Institute would provide a forum for a variety of interactions between conflicting sectors of public and private users of the Lakes, the public and the Center, and the public and the governments responsible for Lakes' management. This Institute would be in a position to perform or sponsor research on sensitive political economic social questions relating

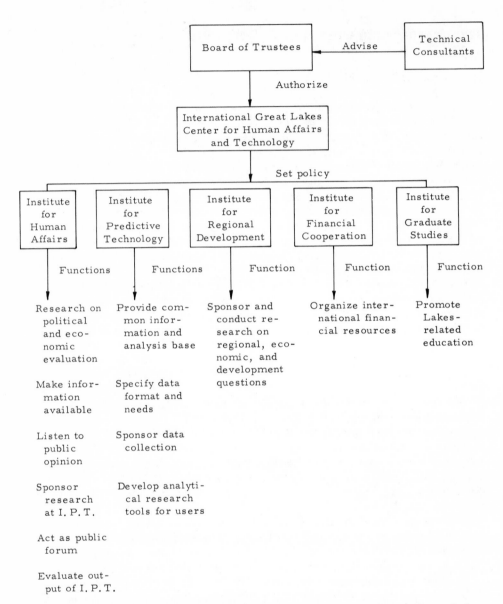

Figure 2-12. Functions of Center Components of the International Great Lakes Center for Human Affairs and Technology

to the Lakes which are unlikely to be adequately investigated otherwise. Finally, this Institute would serve as an auditor or evaluator of information developed in the other Institutes within the Center, particularly the Institute for Predictive Technology. Because better resource management is served by better information available to *all* parties, the Institute for Human Affairs would be responsible for assuring that information pertaining to the Great Lakes, regardless of source, would be made public and available.

Institute for Predictive Technology. The purpose of the Institute for Predictive Technology would be to provide a common basis for advanced technological analyses of the Great Lakes and the Basin. A primary tool of this Institute would be computer-based models developed to enhance capability in understanding all facets of the Great Lakes hydrologic-ecologic-sociological system. This Institute would operate on a user basis, where government agencies, industries, and other interested parties would come to develop the information needed to conduct their respective programs. In addition, research would be sponsored by other Institutes within the Center in the process of carrying out their respective missions. As a technology center for the Great Lakes, this Institute would be a central data bank and would be responsible for developing compatible systems of data acquisition and format. This Institute would be a central mechanism for guidance in field and laboratory research programs needed to improve information systems and could serve as an adviser to key government and private organizations sponsoring research of this type. Where needed, this Institute itself would sponsor research needed to advance its information and prediction capabilities.

The Institute for Predictive Technology would maintain and distribute public compendia of measurements of interest to resource developers and managers in the Basin. Inflation measurements, regional return on investment, construction costs, and other fiscal and technical trend data would be developed and maintained current. This Institute would also offer a modeling and simulation service to users on a cost-incurred basis, which would be available in varying degrees of complexity and scope. No effort would be made to compete with machine operations of industrial concerns providing routine business services.

Institute for Regional Development. One of the major concerns of planners and thinkers in the Great Lakes Basin, and elsewhere, is the extent of regional development considering all relevant factors—population growth and distribution, resource supplies and use, output of wastes, and the growth and use of technological and organizational instruments. It has been indicated, for example, that with proper water resource management the Basin can support ten times its present population. It is important to determine what the population limit is with respect to the use and management of resources and to explore the interrelationship between industrial development and community and scientific growth. These and other concerns of regional economy and development could be considered by the Institute for Regional Development.

Institute for Financial Cooperation. Availability of money will continue to be a problem in achieving the desired quality of living. There will be a continuing need to study alternative methods of financing, getting the vast fiscal resources of the private sector of the economy allocated to the task, and determining equitable cost distribution, tax, and incentive credits. Also, through the institute mechanism, major Lake-related programs could receive international financing. It may be that this could be accomplished through the establishment of a new international bank or fund, not an annex to either country, that could include funds from each and possibly the states and provinces as well as private capital.

Institute for Graduate Studies. Manpower development and utilization of the academic resources in the Basin could be developed in cooperation with existing universities in the Great Lakes Basin. Many of the colleges and universities are prepared to devote their efforts to the solution of complex problems of environmental quality, as indicated recently in a report to the President's Environmental Quality Council (September 1969) entitled "The Universities and Environmental Quality." The pooling of research resources could be the basis for a major interdisciplinary research and training effort.

Center Formation and Support

As presently conceived, formation of an International Great Lakes Center for Human Affairs and Technology would be evolutionary, with none of the institutes being established at the outset. As the function and role to be performed by an institute is clearly defined through additional investigation, it would be formally established and its program managed by the Center. Eventually, when all of the institutes have been created, the Center will become self-sustaining.

Although the Center represents a form of new institution, it should be understood that its creation is not intended to have a constraint on existing institutions or on additional ones being established.

Battelle believes that the activities of the Center, when finally established, must be independent of the influence of its financial supporters. Three primary types of financial support are envisioned to achieve the desired functional relationships within and between the components of the Center: (1) unattached government funds—direct funding from central authorities within the national governments of Canada and the United

States; (2) unattached private funds—funds granted from private, benevolent sources in both countries for independent use by the Center, including Battelle Memorial Institute and major foundations; (3) user funds—funds from users of the Center including government agencies, private concerns, and regional associations or development groups.

Appendixes

Water Pollution in the Great Lakes Basin

C. J. Touhill, M. H. Karr

Virtually every activity pursued by man modifies his environment in some way. While not all of these modifications are detrimental, the sum of discrete activities undertaken to achieve narrow, highly specific goals can be detrimental unless efforts are maintained to balance resource utilization and environmental quality. This balance must be sought with a full understanding of the interactions between resources, benefits, detriments, and long-range costs to society.[2]

Only very recently has the public become aware of the importance of achieving such a balance. Previously, concern for preserving and maintaining our natural resources was subordinated by parochial interests. This shortsightedness has brought our nation to the point where we must consider measures which will cure sicknesses of the environment; preventive measures alone, in many instances, may not be sufficient to avoid passing on a legacy of ruin to future generations.

The five Great Lakes of North America, in varying degrees, serve as an example of misuse and abuse by man. One need only examine the rate of population growth in areas immediately surrounding each of the Lakes with the rate of deterioration of water quality. If the Lakes were ranked according to impaired water quality or interference with beneficial uses, the order would be Lake Erie with the greatest impairment, followed by Lakes Ontario, Michigan, Huron, and Superior. Total population in the drainage basins around each of the lakes very nearly corresponds to this order. The rate of population growth reflects the rate of accelerated aging or eutrophication processes in these lakes.

The resulting conclusion, then, is inescapable: man is directly responsible for the accelerated deterioration of water quality. Moreover, we can also conclude that if action is not taken to protect the lakes from man's infringement, further deterioration will parallel future population growth.

Fortunately, however, this untenable situation has been recognized by all sectors of our society, and preventive measures aimed toward arresting deterioration are presently being implemented. Preventive measures, however, may not be enough. Whether the lakes can recover—Lake Erie in particular—from previous environmental insults through the implementation of preventive measures alone is a subject of considerable conjecture. It is likely that the recovery period would be inordinately long and the foregone benefits considerable. Hence, restoration as well as preventive measures to bring the Great Lakes to a condition where resource utilization and environmental quality can be managed in the best interests of our nation and Canada must be considered.

Aging of the Great Lakes

Current Status

Sophisticated instrumentation is hardly necessary to alert the public to the fact that something has gone awry in Lake Erie. People cannot enjoy its use in the same ways that they could 20 years ago. It is also evident that the southern part of Lake Michigan and parts of Lake Ontario exhibit some of the same symptoms as Lake Erie. Dr. David C. Chandler, Director of the Great Lakes Research Division, Institute of Science and Technology, University of Michigan, in testimony before the Panels on Basic Science and Environmental Problems, Commission on Marine Science, Engineering and Resources, stated that the common denominator limiting the multiple use of the Great Lakes resources is water pollution. Most authorities agree with this conclusion.

In a Federal Water Pollution Control Administration report (1966), "Water Pollution Problems of the Great Lakes Area," the major physical problems of the Great Lakes area are identified as:
—overenrichment of the Lakes;
—build-up of dissolved solids in the Lakes;
—bacterial contamination of the Lakes and tributaries;
—chemical contamination from industrial waste discharges; and
—oxygen depletion of the Lakes and tributaries.

Like all lakes, the Great Lakes are undergoing an aging process that will eventually result in their extinction. Sawyer[2] clearly describes this aging process:

Historically, young lakes are relatively barren bodies of water in terms of the amount of biological life which they support. In this phase they are referred to as being oligotrophic. As aging progresses, the material retained by the lake gradually increases in the bottom sediments and, through bacterial and other decomposition of the sediments, the lake waters become richer and richer in nutrient materials on which phytoplankton thrive. Concurrent with the increase in phytoplankton, the population of zooplankton and higher animal forms responds accordingly, as the food supply gains in amount.

With the increase in biological productivity of a lake, major changes occur in both the surface and deeper waters. The lake passes from the oligotrophic phase through the mesotrophic and finally into the eutrophic phase. It continues in this phase until deposits from biological activity, both organic and inorganic, plus materials settled from the tributary waters, fill the basin to the extent that rooted aquatic plants take command of the situation and gradually convert the area to marsh land.

The aging process is commonly referred to as eutrophication, for which Stewart and Rohlich[3] give the following definition: "The process of enrichment with nutrients." Accelerated eutrophication or overenrichment of the lakes results from the input of nutrient materials, mainly nitrogen and phosphorus, from the activities of man. Normally, the natural aging process proceeds at the slow pace measured by the geological time scale. However, man has so accelerated this time scale, through his discharge of nutrients to the Lakes, that significant aging can be observed within a generation.

Accelerated eutrophication is given principal emphasis because it is the most critical problem, in terms of impairment of benefits, facing the Great Lakes. It is one of the most difficult problems whose remedy will require application of a number of curative measures. Also, it can be shown that other problems such as buildup of dissolved solids and oxygen depletion are closely intertwined with eutrophication.

Accelerated eutrophication of Lake Erie is manifest in the following ways:

(1) Blue-green algal blooms and other algal groups such as diatoms produce noxious odors and at times appear as unsightly scums on the water surface.

(2) These same algae impart unpleasant tastes to water supplies.

(3) Dissolved oxygen levels are depressed in thermally stratified areas.

(4) Bottom-dwelling fauna change from clean water forms to less desirable forms that are tolerant to pollution and low oxygen concentration.

(5) Fisheries resources have changed from highly prized game fish, such as pike, trout, and whitefish, to the coarse, less valuable fish such as carp, catfish, and sheepshead.

(6) Nuisance filamentous algae growing in shallow waters near shore, break loose, and wash up onto the shores and beaches.

(7) Unsightly, odorous conglomerates of algal and other pollutants interfere with the recreational use of waters and beaches, clog municipal and industrial water intakes, and depress property values.

Water quality assessments indicated that nearly all of Lake Erie is eutrophic, Lake Ontario is on the verge of becoming eutrophic, and Lake Michigan is exhibiting some of the symptoms of eutrophy in certain areas, particularly in the southwestern portion of the Lake. Isolated examples of pollution have been observed in Lakes Huron and Superior although, in general, water quality in these Lakes is considered good.

The reader is referred to an excellent paper by Beeton [4] for a detailed discussion of the indices of eutrophication in the Great Lakes.

Increases in the dissolved solids concentration in certain of the Great Lakes have been observed over the years since routine water quality analyses were first initiated. Despite the fact that dissolved solids concentrations have not seriously impaired water uses, localized problems, influenced by population and industrial growth, are being experienced near points of large waste discharges. It is likely that the dissolved solids problem will be remedied in part by implementation of recently adopted state water quality standards.

Because most bacterial contamination of the Great Lakes can be directly traced to man, it can likewise be remedied more easily.

Oxygen depletion of the Great Lakes and their tributaries is a twofold problem. Oxygen can be depleted through (1) the addition of organic substances to the receiving bodies of water; and (2) the proliferation of algae associated with eutrophic conditions. Organic pollutants, where controllable, can be dealt with by implementing treatment methods consistent with water quality standards.

In summary, use of the resources of the Great Lakes is limited by water pollution. Although a variety of classes of pollution are evident, the most serious, long-range problem results from accelerated eutrophication, or the aging process, of these Lakes.

Causes

The principal nutrients of concern in the enrichment process of eutrophication are phosphorus and nitrogen compounds. Other nutrients have also been implicated as contributing to accelerated eutrophication, including vitamins, growth hormones, and amino acids. In addition, trace elements are known to play a major role in the process, but their relative importance is ill-defined.

As Martin and Weinberger [5] stated:

Bodies of water contain a constantly changing biological system composed of many microscopic and macroscopic life forms. These species are interrelated and depend on the condition of the total ecological balance of the environment for their existences. The biological system is dynamic, is complex, involves biochemical interrelationships among the life forms in the water itself, and involves chemical and hydrologic interactions between the bottom sediments and the water. Four factors that influence the aquatic ecological balance are: the concentration of suspended and dissolved organic and inorganic compounds, the availability of these compounds as nutrient material, the concentration of dissolved gases including oxygen, and the availability of sunlight.

Various methods of assessment are employed to determine the degree of eutrophication that exists in a receiving body of water. A compilation of these by Sawyer is shown below.[6]

> Hypolimnetic (for example, bottom water) Oxygen
> > Dissolved
> > Rate of consumption
> Biological Productivity
> > Standing crop
> > Volume of algae

      Transparency
      Chlorophyll in epilimnion (surface water)
      Oxygen production
      Carbon dioxide utilization
  Nutrient Levels
      Nitrogen
      Phosphorus
      Nitrogen-phosphorus ratios

The accelerated aging or eutrophication of certain of the Great Lakes is not the sole cause or symptom of deterioration of water quality. However, because the effects of other pollutants are so intimately linked to this phenomenon, measures implemented to prevent accelerated eutrophication and to restore the water quality in eutrophic lakes will help to improve other water quality problems such as oxygen depletion caused by the biodegradation of organic wastes.

In order to define required action, including the formulation of restoration methods, it is essential to have an adequate understanding of the nature of causative factors. The following discussion identifies known factors contributing to accelerated aging of the Great Lakes, and examines the relative influence of each factor upon the rate of aging.

Municipal Wastewater. Because nitrogen can be fixed directly from the atmosphere by biological life, phosphorus takes on increasing importance as a more readily controllable nutrient. Municipal wastewater, mainly sewage, is the dominant source of nutrients, especially phosphorus, in the Great Lakes. For example, an FWQA survey has shown that 75 percent of the phosphorus added to Lake Erie annuatlly comes from municipal wastewater. Moreover, about 66 percent of the phosphorus is associated with detergents. Approximately two-thirds of this nutrient is retained in the Lake, principally by incorporation in bottom sediments.

Needless to say, the municipal wastewater discharges have had a drastic effect on the aging of the Great Lakes—Lake Erie, in particular. There can be no doubt that the discharge of domestic sewage has been a predominating contributor to the deterioration of water quality, not only because of nutrients but also because of bacterial and organic contamination.

Whereas eutrophication is measured on a geological time scale under natural conditions, accelerated eutrophication resulting from man's activities can be evident in a single lifetime.

Combined Storm Sewage. Combined storm sewage sometimes constitutes a more severe problem than municipal wastewater. Many communities have been vigorous in instituting the most modern technology for wastewater treatment. However, where sewage treatment plants receive combined storm sewage, a heavy rainfall can overtax the hydraulic capability of the treatment plant so that substantial wastewater flows are directly bypassed to receiving bodies of water.

Many factors are involved in assessing the impact of such discharges to the Great Lakes, but it is quite clear that the total effect will be one which approximates the magnitude of municipal wastewater during periods of high rainfall. If this contributor of nutrients were the principal one, aging would not be accelerated as greatly as for municipal wastewater, but perceptible changes in water quality deterioration in the Great Lakes would result. The aging process would certainly be slower than that caused by direct discharge of municipal wastewater, but would be considerably faster than that occurring naturally on the geological time scale.

Industrial Wastewater. Quite often industrial wastes are routed to municipal treatment systems for the mutual benefit of the community and its industry. In this situation, such effluents have the effect discussed under municipal wastewaters.

Since many large industries border the Great Lakes, it is usually more economical for these industries to pursue effluent treatment within their own complex. Federal Water Pollution Control Administration surveys have shown that many of these industries do not effect a suitable degree of treatment. In the context of this appendix, many types of inadequately treated effluents can contribute to accelerated eutrophication. Examples are: nutrient-laden effluents, organic contaminants, noxious chemicals, and sediments or inorganic residues.

In terms of their contribution to accelerated eutrophication, industrial wastewater discharges in the Great Lakes as a whole will have less effect on the aging rate than does municipal wastewater. Rather, a chronic and generally localized deterioration occurs. Whether accelerated aging would be evident is dependent upon the volumes of wastewater discharged and the amounts of nutrients associated with these discharges.

Watercraft Wastes. At the present time, wastes from watercraft are not treated to the extent that municipal wastewaters are, or, in the majority of cases, not at all. In the United States, recreational watercraft wastes are equivalent to the wastewater discharged by a community of 500,000. Extrapolated to the Great Lakes area, this contribution to water quality deterioration is insignificant by comparison with other nutrient sources. While it is beneficial, particularly from a public health standpoint, to require treatment of watercraft wastes—an objective of the Federal Water Pollution Control Administration—it is extremely doubtful whether watercraft wastes would accelerate eutrophication in the Great Lakes if this were the sole source of nutrients. Of course, the problem will grow in magnitude as water transportation and recreational boating increase.

Oil Discharges. Oil discharges to the Great Lakes are undesirable because of the ecological imbalances that occur and because of the drastic effects on aesthetics. The literature shows that small amounts of oil can be readily observed as slicks. For example, a discharge of only 50 gallons of oil can be visually observed when dispersed over an area of 1 square mile. On the other hand, the total effect of oil discharges upon eutrophication could be somewhat beneficial because the amount of sunlight, critical to the proliferation of algae, will be reduced.

It should be clearly understood, however, that despite the fact that there might be some arresting of the eutrophication problem, the associated water quality impairment and loss of benefits from oil discharges far overshadow meager improvements. Oil sludge deposits actually represent an advanced state of aging in the form of undecomposed organic matter.

Dredging. It has been common practice for many years to dredge harbors and channels of the Great Lakes to provide suitable drafts for transport vessels. The dredgings are usually comprised of silt and sediments, carried by tributary streams and rivers, and sewage and industrial waste residues. These dredgings are particularly rich in nutrients. Past practice has been to discharge the dredgings back to Lake waters. This often releases more nutrients to the Lakes than would normally occur had the deposited sediments and residues been undistrubed.

As stated previously, about two-thirds of the phosphorus discharged to Lake Erie is retained within the Lake. The bottom sediments are the repository for this nutrient. Hence, dredging causes an increase in the recycling of sediment stored nutrients by exposing more surface area.

Eutrophication will definitely be accelerated by dredging, particularly in the disturbed area. It is anticipated that if large areas are disturbed and if the associated dredgings are reintroduced to the Lake, measurable increase in the aging process will occur.

By the same token, if the dredgings are removed to land and isolated from leaching and runoff to receiving bodies of water, significant long-range benefits will accrue.

Thermal Discharges. Thermal discharges can have both beneficial and detrimental effects in terms of accelerated eutrophication. Discharge of heated effluents such as industrial and power plant cooling water can induce algal blooms during periods of the year when water temperatures are not normally high enough to permit algae growth. On the other hand, during the time of the year when the most critical problems of accelerated eutrophication are manifest, thermal discharges could be used to help destratify the Lakes. Stratification causes oxygen deficiencies in the hypolimnion, the bottom region of the Lake. The oxygen deficiency, in turn, causes vastly increased recycle of nutrients from the bottom sediments and is frequently referred to as the most critical period in the annual aging cycle.

Hence, it appears that accelerated eutrophication of the Great Lakes could be increased or decreased, depending upon how thermal discharges are managed.

Nutrient-Laden Inflow From Tributaries. In some instances, inflow from tributaries and impoundments are sources of nutrients to the Great Lakes. Because impoundments suffer the same problems of aging that the Lakes do, both the causes and remedies will be very nearly the same as those for the Great Lakes. This illustrates the need to deal with the Great Lakes as a total basin, thereby implementing preventive and restorative measures for tributaries as well as for the Lakes themselves. This aspect is further discussed under agricultural runoff.

Ducks and Other Waterfowl. The Great Lakes are used extensively by migratory waterfowl and serve as a habitat area for large numbers of waterfowl. While such birds contribute to the eutrophication of the Lakes, one could justifiably say that waterfowl do not constitute a problem beyond the natural aging process.

Where waterfowl are cultivated for commercial purposes, such as near Moriches Bay on Long Island, man does in fact have control. Because this activity is not evident on any appreciable scale in the Great Lakes area, there does not appear to be an impact of this sort other than from wild waterfowl.

Fisheries Considerations. That fisheries have suffered from water quality deterioration in the Great Lakes is well known. Actually, the annual production of fish in Lake Erie based on catch of all species has not decreased concommitant with accelerated eutrophication. The Lake Erie catch remains at about 500 million pounds per year. What has changed, however, is the species of fish with less desirable varieties supplanting the more desirable game fish. This is because spawning and rearing areas have been inundated by water of inferior quality and the game species have failed to reproduce. In Lake Erie, the bottom fauna has been modified by pollutants and sediments so that the game and fish food supply has been altered and only the more tolerant species which are the less desirable can thrive in such an environment.

The predation of sea lamprey has had some impact, but this has been less important recently in Lake Erie than in Lakes Michigan and Superior.

A common technique employed to increase fish production in lakes has been the purposeful addition of nutrients. It must be recognized that the removal of fish by catches also constitutes a removal of nutrients. This fact has importance in the Great Lakes for a number of reasons. First, the planned use of fisheries resources can be beneficial in nutrient control.

For example, it is readily apparent that measures must be instituted to remove nutrients as part of any restoration technique. For this reason, the alewife problem in Lake Michigan is an important area from the standpoint of accelerated eutrophication. Dead alewives that wash ashore must be removed; otherwise they will be a potent source of nutrients.

Likewise, alewives can also be a source of protein for the undernourished of the world. Therefore, through reasonable planning and management, two functions can be carried out simultaneously. First, nutrient removal can be accomplished by a vigorous fishery for so-called undesirable species; and second, these fish can furnish a significant amount of protein.

Sedimentation. The preceding discussion has identified municipal wastewater as the principal source of nutrients in the Great Lakes. Sedimentation, including silts, erosion and agricultural runoff, dead biological life, and wastewater residues, constitutes the second most important source of nutrients.

As silts and erosion runoff flow into the lake, nutrients are dissolved and are available for biological utilization. Land use practices, especially land development practices in urban areas as well as agricultural areas, have all contributed to the problem. If measures are not undertaken to control this nutrient source, accelerated eutrophication will be rapid, second only to municipal wastewater effects.

Resulting sediment deposits form vast nutrient reservoirs that take on increasing importance during those periods of the year when hypolimnetic (bottom water) oxygen is deficient or nonexistent. An example of their importance is illustrated by a present program conducted by the FWQA in Klamath Lake, Oregon. This Lake was selected for study because of evidence of eutrophic conditions in the presence of minimal influence by man. It is essentially a naturally eutrophic Lake. FWQA scientists have determined that if all nutrient input to the Lake ceased, there would still be sufficient nutrient inventory stored in the upper one inch of sediments to provide for the nutrient requirements of the Lake for 60 years. Dr. A. F. Bartsch, Chief of the National Eutrophication Research Program, FWQA, has established a high priority for research aimed toward determining how much of this nutrient is available through the sediment-water interchange.

Agricultural Runoff. Agricultural runoff has also been identified as a significant source of nutrients entering the Great Lakes. The runoff is comprised of eroded soil, leached salts and fertilizers, and excess fertilizer. Measures which can be taken to alleviate some of the nutrient contribution from agricultural runoff include land management techniques (contour plowing, for example), judicious fertilizer application, and controlled water addition where possible. Because treatment methods cannot be applied to point sources, it is difficult to control nutrients in agricultural runoff. This problem is a major one in terms of accelerated eutrophication of the Great Lakes. It probably is of the same magnitude as combined storm sewage.

The amount of nutrients found in animal manure has been estimated by the FWQA staff. In the Midwest alone it is estimated that the nutrient content for animal wastes is equivalent to 300 million people. While it is obvious that only a fraction reaches the Great Lakes, the potential from this source is staggering.

In actual fact, the rate of aging of the Great Lakes has not been significantly increased because of animal wastes and manure, but measurable increases in the rate of eutrophication can be attributed to agricultural drainage.

Urban Land Drainage. This problem is to be distinguished from combined storm sewage which, in some ways, has many similar elements. In this case, the assumption is made that a separate sewerage system exists for storm runoff.

Urban or storm drainage is composed of many types of potential nutrient sources. Street sediments, grit, oils, salts, and refuse are washed from the streets to the drainage system. The effluent is usually discharged directly to a receiving body of water because the contamination potential of pathogens from this type of drainage is quite low. The nutrient concentration might not be low, particularly in rich soil areas. In terms of impact on the aging of the Great Lakes, urban land drainage would probably have an effect similar to that of combined storm sewage.

Subsurface Waste Disposal. Many of the developing areas around the Great Lakes as well as the rural regions have employed septic fields for domestic wastewater disposal. In porous strata or in areas with poor soil exchange capacity, nutrients in substantial amounts drain to the Lakes. In general, these regions are fairly well dispersed and do not constitute a major source of nutrients. It is not anticipated that this source of nutrients will have a major effect on the aging process.

Atmospheric-Quality Deterioration. Scientific investigators have shown that the levels of carbon dioxide are increasing in the atmosphere, although the measurable increase is rather small. It has been shown that the mean temperature of the atmosphere has likewise increased. Again, the increase is small. Furthermore, the level of a variety of contaminants has increased commensurate with the population growth of the world.

All of these factors do, in fact, subtly modify the earth's total ecological balance. But there are no scientific tools available with which to perceive or measure any short-range imbalances that might occur. By comparison with other massive environmental insults, it is improbable that atmospheric deterioration through the activities of man will truly accelerate aging of the Great Lakes measurably in the near future.

The preceding discussion has endeavored to establish the relative importance of the various causes for aging of the Great Lakes. It must be realized that it is virtually impossible to predict what would happen to the eutrophication trend through removal of any single nutrient source. While priorities should be established to deal with both preventive and restorative techniques, many methods will have to be implemented before an effective restoration program can be achieved.

In summary, the aforementioned contributors to eutrophication are ranked according to their ability to contribute, either individually or in combination, toward accelerated aging, and hence serve as the target for both preventive and restorative measures.

> *High Impact*
> Municipal Wastewater
> Agricultural Runoff
> Sediment Interchange
> *Medium Impact*
> Industrial Wastewater
> Combined Storm Sewage
> Urban Land Drainage
> Dredging
> Tributary Inflow
> Fisheries Considerations
> *Low Impact*
> Watercraft Wastes
> Oil Discharges
> Waterfowl
> Subsurface Disposal
> Atmospheric-Quality Deterioration

Obviously, this ranking is very general, and for localized problems it might be inappropriate, but for the Great Lakes it is indicative of orders of magnitude.

Prevention and Restoration Technology

The fundamental question facing those concerned with arresting accelerated aging of the Great Lakes is: "Can the eutrophication process be reversed?" The question is an extremely significant one because the level of effort and funds expended on Great Lakes restoration are dependent upon the answer. In a recent issue of *Water in the News,* compiled by the Soap and Detergent Association, Dr. Ralph O. Brinkhurst, Professor of Zoology at the University of Toronto, has provided a very emphatic answer.

In referring to Lake Erie, Dr. Brinkhurst said, "It's the healthiest corpse I've seen." He firmly believes that eutrophication can be reversed, and has cited specific studies which demonstrate that eutrophication reversal has occurred in the past in other lakes, although none the size of the Great Lakes.

The fact that the FWQA and numerous other researchers are working toward objectives which will control factors contributing to eutrophication and help to restore optimal water quality reinforces Dr. Brinkhurst's conclusion.

Technology to control eutrophication can be categorized as either preventive or restorative. Quite simply, preventive measures are employed to remove nutrients before discharge to a receiving body of water, and restorative measures are used to remove the nutrients or the products of eutrophy from the affected body of water. Measures which are directed at reducing nutrient inputs are also generally of value in improving other water quality parameters, for example, bacterial content, which may have little bearing on eutrophication per se.

Preventive Measures

In general, preventive measures fall into two categories: (1) nutrient exclusion; and (2) nutrient diversion.

Nutrient Exclusion. Because the major source of nutrients is municipal wastewater, most research has been directed toward developing suitable methods for removing nutrients from this particular type of waste. Most of the methods identified, however, can also be applied to other nutrient-containing aqueous streams.

Because detergents account for a substantial portion of the phosphorus in municipal wastewater, the soap and detergent industry is vigorously studying compounds which may be substitued for phosphate as sequestering agents.

The following tabulation, compiled from data by Martin and Weinberger,[7] shows the efficiencies of various nutrient removal processes.

Recently it has been shown that activated sludge secondary treatment plants can be operated in such a manner that nutrient removal is optimized. Aeration rate, aeration time, aeration solids, and return sludge ratios are all critical parameters in determining the degree of phosphorus removal. Activated sludge plants can also be operated to accentuate denitrification. A variety of different operating procedures has been suggested for this purpose.

The wide variations in nutrient removal using the activated sludge method are due to the fact that operating procedures control the degree of efficiency. Several procedures control the degree of efficiency. Several

Table A-1
Efficiency of Two Nutrient Removal Processes

Method	Total Nitrogen Removal, percent	Total Phosphorus Removal, percent
Activated sludge	20–82	10–80
Algae removal systems	35–95	41–100
Chemical precipitation	12–68	78–100
Ion exchange	82–99.5	95–99.6
Membrane processes	50	50
Ammonia stripping	82–98 (NH_3)	—
Effluent land spraying	54–68	76–93
Distillation	75	96

investigators have suggested that optimized nutrient removal for both phosphorus and nitrogen is not possible by this method. They have suggested further that the plants should be operated for maximum phosphorus removal.

Since the nutrients in municipal wastewaters cause algal blooms in receiving bodies of water, a method has been developed whereby algae are cultured under controlled conditions. The algae are then harvested in this treatment process so that the resulting effluent will be low in nutrient content. The limiting factor in the removal of nitrogen and phosphorus has been the efficiency of algal harvesting techniques.

Chemical precipitation with the hydrous oxides of aluminum and iron and with lime has been highly effective in removing phosphorus from municipal wastewater. Nitrogen removal by this method has been somewhat less effective. The method is an attractive one because of ease of operation and relative low cost.

Of all potential nutrient removal processes, ion exchange has been demonstrated to be most effective for both nitrogen and phosphorus removal. On the other hand, ion exchange is expensive and requires extensive pretreatment for effective operation.

While membrane processes are primarily employed for total dissolved solids removal, they do have capability for some degree of nitrogen and phosphorus removal. Since only about 50 percent of both nutrients are removed by electrodialysis, a membrane process, the method is usually employed only in conjunction with other treatment requirements. This method is also rather expensive.

Ammonia stripping has been effective in removing ammonia nitrogen from wastewater effluents. This method has most often been employed in conjunction with other efforts to prepare wastewater for reuse or reclamation.

Effluent spraying on land has likewise been relatively effective in removing nutrients from municipal wastewater. Care must be taken, however, to assure that drainage from the irrigated land does not eventually find its way to a receiving body of water. This method is the least costly of those identified as having potential.

Distillation results, as one would imagine, in efficient removal of both nitrogen and phosphorus, with phosphorus removals being the highest, that is, greater than 95 percent. On the other hand, it is quite costly and is usually regarded as a method held in abeyance until others have been demonstrated to be inappropriate.

Other methods have been proposed, but most are still in the research or developmental stage. Recent FWQA Hearings on Lake Michigan will no doubt accelerate efforts to evolve an efficient, inexpensive method for phosphorus removal. The Secretary of the Interior, in his recommendations resulting from the Hearings, has stated that phosphorus removal from municipal wastewater should be maximized, and by 1972, 80 percent removal of phosphorus should be provided by municipalities that discharge effluents to Lake Michigan.

Assuming that nutrient removal is accomplished in municipal wastewater treatment plants, further nutrient exclusion can be effected by the institution of plans to accommodate in these plants the maximum amount of combined storm sewage from existing sewerage systems. Also, wherever possible, treatable industrial wastes should be accommodated by municipal wastewater treatment plants. Specific recommendations have been proposed for both of these plants as a result of the Lake Michigan Hearings. To further implement nutrient exclusion plans, the Secretary of the Interior recommended that all new sewer construction be planned in such a manner that only separated storm and sanitary sewerage systems are constructed.

Agricultural runoff, which is also a significant source of nutrients, is more difficult to control. However, certain measures can be taken to provide nutrient exclusion. Land management practices can be implemented to prevent erosion and subsequent pollution by siltation. Wherever possible, water applied to crops can be managed to minimize leaching of fertilizers from soils. In concert with these efforts, more judicious use of fertilizers, either chemical or animal, would minimize the unnecessary addition of excess fertilizer to streams or lakes. Essential to the implementation of this objective is a more rigorous knowledge of the nutrient requirements of crops. Manure piles at dairy farms contribute large amounts of nutrient owing to uncontrolled runoff during periods of precipitation. Research to provide a solution to this problem is in progress.

Measures are presently under way to control the discharge of watercraft wastes. Alternatives considered are: (1) retention of wastes onboard the watercraft with subsequent shore-based treatment, including nutrient removal; or (2) onboard treatment equivalent to secondary treatment and a correspondingly high degree of nutrient treatment. Considerable research and development is now under way, sponsored by the FWQA, Navy, and Coast Guard.

Another measure which can be implemented to exclude nutrients from the Great Lakes is the cessation of dredging and garbage, trash, and refuse disposal to the Lakes. Of these, dredging has caused concern in localized areas because of the amount of potential nutrients associated with this material. The problem is well recognized and action has been taken to implement programs for the cessation of such disposal practices. Care must be exercised in the land disposal of dredgings so that leaching and subsequent runoff do not create problems at a later time.

Nutrient Diversion. A technique which has been successfully employed in the past to prevent accelerated eutrophication is the diversion of nutrient-containing sources, such as municipal wastewater, around bodies of water which potentially could be affected. Despite the success of this method, it can prove to be a shortsighted remedy. First of all, the problem is merely passed on to someone else, usually to a downstream impoundment, lake, bay, or estuary. In terms of total resource management, this is not an acceptable solution unless there are substantial mitigating circumstances for which the long-term effects are thoroughly understood.

A second disadvantage is the loss of use of the diverted water. Maximum beneficial use of water can be constrained purely from the standpoint of quantity despite quality considerations. Navigation is an excellent example. Therefore, while nutrient diversion can help localized problems, the diseconomies and imbalances in total resource management which might result could far overshadow the benefits.

Restorative Measures

As with preventive measures, restorative ones are designed to remove nutrients from water, the difference being largely a matter of scale. Where prevention deals with waste streams up to millions of gallons per day, restoration in the Great Lakes could deal with hundreds of cubic miles of water. This point should be carefully remembered when alternative courses of action are considered.

Some of the restorative techniques discussed below are based on limnological theory rather than on actual experimental or developmental work. Others are based on applications to lakes of much smaller size than the Great Lakes.

Sealing of the Bottom Sediments. Even if extensive measures were implemented to prevent the addition of any nutrients, recycling of nutrients from previously deposited sediments could continue the accelerated eutrophication process for a considerable period of time.

Although quantitative data are deficient, research has shown that nutrient availability at the sediment-water interface can be a key factor in accelerated eutrophication. During periods of the year when oxygen deficiencies are observed in the hypolimnion (the bottom region of the lake), deposited ferric iron is reduced to the soluble ferrous species. Water quality surveys have shown that an appreciable increase in the nutrient content of the overlying waters occurs, presumably due to release from bottom sediments. If the bottom of the lake could be coated or sealed, the nutrient in the sediments would not be available.

This sealing would have to be renewed periodically, perhaps even annually, if concomitant measures were not implemented to prevent the accumulation of additional nutrients from such things as silt, dead algae, and other aquatic life.

Flushing With Low-Nutrient Water. A technique which has been employed to restore water quality with some degree of success is the use of low-nutrient water to flush eutrophic lakes. Such a method has been used in Green Lake in Seattle, and the FWQA is presently planning similar experiments in Moses Lake, Washington.

Since appreciable quantities of low-nutrient water are required, the practicality of using this method in the Great Lakes is questionable. It is also possible that downstream lakes will be adversely affected by the flushed nutrients.

Nutrient Removal. It was stated earlier that about two-thirds of the phosphorus introduced into Lake Erie is retained, mostly in the bottom sediments. Significant amounts are also retained by fish, algae, and rooted vegetation. Removal of fish will be dealt with in later discussions.

Both algae and aquatic weeds (macrophytes) have been harvested in lakes for nutrient removal. Several notable problem areas have come to light because of this previous experience. Algae harvesting is a difficult and tedious task. Blue-green algae, the principal biota indicative of eutrophication, float, but removal by skimming or filtration is complicated by apparatus fouling. Harvesting is slow and only small areas can be covered by presently available equipment.

Greater success has been observed for aquatic-weed harvesting, but still, the job is a slow and arduous one. Some investigators are presently evaluating designs for more effective weed harvesters which will be capable of dealing with large areas in shorter periods of time.

It is essential that algae and aquatic weeds be removed from the Lake. In some cases, nuisance aquatic weeds have been cut and allowed to remain in the water; hence, no nutrient removal was effected. Furthermore, the harvested algae and weeds must be disposed of in such a fashion that leaching and drainage will not permit reentry of nutrients to the Lake. One solution would be to utilize them as protein sources, fertilizer, mulch, or animal feeds.

Thermal Destratification. As discussed, during periods of the year when oxygen deficiencies are observed in the hypolimnion, nutrient availability at the sediment-water interface is greatly increased. These oxygen deficiencies result largely from thermal stratification and oxygen consumption from biological decay on the lake bottom. Research results show that destratification, and thus oxygenation, may reduce the availability of nutrients in bottom sediments, thereby arresting or retarding eutrophication.

The theory advanced to explain this phenomenon is related to the solubility of iron and, to some extent, manganese. During periods of oxygen deficiency, insoluble trivalent iron and tetravalent manganese are reduced to their soluble ferrous and manganese species. To illustrate, in the presence of oxygen, ferric phosphate and ferric hydroxide prevent phosphorus from entering the overlying water by compound formation or coating action, respectively. Under reducing conditions, when oxygen is absent, ferrous iron enters solution and exposes the sediments and releasing bound phosphate.

Destratification can be accomplished in three ways: (1) mechanical mixing; (2) aeration mixing; and (3) thermal mixing. In the first case, the lake is mechanically stirred so that the three zones of stratification, the epilimnion, thermocline, and hypolimnion, are thoroughly mixed. In the second case, the same mixing effect is reached, but in addition the water is oxygenated. In thermal mixing, heated water generates the mixing effect that causes destratification.

Dredging. Since bottom sediments represent such a potent source of nutrients, removal of the sediments has been recommended as a method for restoring lakes to the oligotrophic state. In the Great Lakes, however, sediments are quite thick in certain areas. This, combined with the expanse of the Lakes, dictates that herculean efforts would be required to completely remove the sediments. Care would have to be exercised to minimize release of nutrients during the dredging operation.

Biological Control. Biological control of algae and aquatic weeds is possible if suitable animal populations are discovered which are capable of grazing on the blue-green algae and rooted vegetation. Another approach would be to develop strains of viruses or parasites that prey exclusively on the algae and aquatic weeds. Research is under way to attain these objectives, but there has been very little success to date.

Chemical Control. For almost a century, copper sulfate has been used as an algacide. Although copper sulfate has been very successful in controlling algae blooms, it is also toxic to other life forms. Research investigators are seeking to discover algacides which are highly specific, killing only the noxious species of concern.

Chemical control is not a nutrient-removal method. In fact, only the symptoms of eutrophication are treated. Dead algae settle to the lake bottom increasing the potential nutrient reservoir in the sediments. It is only a temporary measure and must be repeated at frequent intervals. Also, the chemicals might be accumulated in fish and eventually be harmful to man.

Chemical Inactivation. Research is also under way to find a method to chemically inactivate the nutrients. The aim is to find a compound which, when added to the body of water, will either complex or somehow combine chemically with the nutrients, preventing utilization by algae. One potential method is to develop chelating agents which will complex with divalent ions. The divalent cations function as coenzymes in nitrogen fixation by algae, and they determine the types of algae growths which result. Hence, the algae will be nutrient-limited and eutrophication will be retarded. Biologically stable chelators are presently available.

Prevention of Light Penetration. The development of a substance which will decrease the penetration of light into the Lakes by increasing either reflectance or opacity has been proposed. This substance would have to be (1) nontoxic; (2) biologically stable; and (3) nonrestrictive to oxygen transfer into the water. No known substance satisfies these criteria or others required to maintain maximum beneficial use of the water resource. A serious consequence from adding such a substance would be the potential interference with all photosynthesis. During certain periods of the year, photosynthetic organisms can provide measurable quantities of oxygen to lakes, particularly during hours of sunlight.

Rough Fish Removal. Part of the nutrient inventory in the Great Lakes is retained by the fish population. Obviously, one way to reduce the nutrient inventory is to remove the fish. However, many of the fish species in the Lakes are highly desirable for game or commerce. On the other hand, there are substantial populations of rough fish such as carp and alewives which are undesirable. Alewives, in particular, have caused substantial problems in Lake Michigan.

A concerted effort to remove these fish would result in a reduction of nutrients potentially available for eutrophication. Because burial of the fish within the Great Lakes Basin could again allow the nutrients to be reintroduced to the Lakes, it would be prudent to consider the use of these fish as a source of protein.

Since desirable fish species are also a nutrient source, it might be desirable to encourage increased harvesting. Implementation of such a plan would have to balance nutrient removal and species propagation.

Other Measures for Water Quality
Improvement

Accelerated eutrophication is not the only cause of water quality deterioration in the Great Lakes. Although the aging process can produce the most serious long-range consequences, the beneficial uses of the Great Lakes can be interfered with in other ways as well.

Most of the improvement measures cited below are recommendations of the Federal Water Quality Administration and others as part of the continuing study of the Great Lakes Basin.

Municipal Wastewater Treatment. A minimum of secondary treatment should be provided by municipalities discharging wastewater to the Great Lakes. Treatment should be efficient and continuous and should provide for 90 percent removal of oxygen-consuming wastes. Limits should be recommended for specific pollutants such as suspended solids, settleable solids, ammonia, phenolics, oil, and those exerting a biochemical oxygen demand. These limits should be set at a level commensurate with their ability to interfere with the beneficial uses of water.

Whenever possible, treatable industrial wastes should be accommodated by municipal wastewater treatment systems, and master plans for integrated treatment facilities in urban areas should be formulated. Areas with septic tank disposal systems should be incorporated into sewerage systems as soon as possible.

Continuous disinfection of all municipal wastewater also should be effected as soon as possible.

Industrial Wastewater Treatment. All industrial wastes should receive the equivalent of secondary treatment, and those industrial wastes which cause chemical pollution should be either excluded from the Lakes or receive a suitable high level of treatment.

Maximum reduction by the best available treatment should be implemented for the following wastes: acids and alkalies, oils and tarry substances, phenolic compounds and other organics which produce taste and odor problems, ammonia and other nitrogen compounds, phosphorus, suspended materials, toxic and highly colored materials, oxygen-demanding substances, excessive heat, foam-producing compounds, and other materials which detract from aesthetics or other beneficial uses of water.

Agricultural Runoff. Pesticides and herbicides should be applied to land in such a fashion as to minimize the amounts that reach the Great Lakes as surface or subsurface runoff.

Thermal Discharges. Thermal discharges should be managed in such a way that water quality standards are met, and these discharges are beneficially employed wherever possible.

Oil Discharges. Treatment of oil and other hazardous materials should be undertaken so that these materials will be excluded from the Great Lakes.

Degree of Restoration

The foregoing sections have shown that (1) the causes of water quality deterioration in the Great Lakes are fairly well defined; (2) technology is available for preventing most of the water quality problems; and (3) technology for restoring Great Lakes water quality has been or can be developed. Significant preventive measures are now being implemented to improve Great Lakes water quality. There can be no doubt that Lake Erie will become dystrophic and truly dead if accelerated eutrophication is allowed to proceed unimpeded.

If only preventive measures are implemented, this would parallel the condition where technology for improvement is only partially applied. From the best available information, it is speculated that the Great Lakes could be restored to a desired level of water quality, but only after a substantial period of time. Some even speculate that recovery would be measured in terms of geological time.

Even if technology for improvement is fully applied, that is, full utilization of preventive and restorative technology, restoration of desirable water quality could take as long as a generation. This, of course, presumes that eutrophication is reversible—a point that has generated considerable controversy. However, recent research appears to confirm that reversal of eutrophication is, to some degree, possible.

Therefore, in summary, if present resource management practices are not improved, Lake Erie will continue to accelerate toward its demise, and the other Lakes will likely succumb further in the future in the order Ontario, Michigan, Huron, and Superior. If only preventive measures are taken, Lake Erie may recover in a few thousand years, and water quality in other Lakes will be maintained. Lake Ontario may also show improvement. If both preventive and restorative measures are implemented, marked improvement in Lake Erie might be observed within a generation.

These statements, however, are far too general to support the necessity for restoration. The question, What is the desired level of water quality in the Great Lakes? has never been specifically answered. It would appear that the objective should be to optimize the benefits which would accrue because of enhanced water quality in terms of the cost of attaining such enhancement.

Kneese [8] has stated essentially the same thing:

Within the general framework of a market system, there are rather clear-cut reasons to suppose that public intervention can improve performance with respect to disposal of wastes into water bodies. Not only can government intervention improve efficiency as measured in terms of market values, but it can and should take explicit cognizance of extra-market values. Since the character of water courses in heavily populated areas is such that interdependency between uses is inevitable, a major problem confronting public policy is to gauge accurately the significance of various interdependencies and foster the efficient multipurpose use of the water resource.

The answer, then, to the question of how much restoration is enough can be determined through a detailed benefit-cost analysis similar to that which has long been used to evaluate the economic feasibility of large public projects.

The first two steps would be to (1) evaluate the cost of measures employed to enhance water quality to various levels, both preventive and restorative; and (2) evaluate the benefits accruing to society owing to improved water quality at these levels resulting from the implementation of improvement measures.

Figure A-1 illustrates the type of analysis required. It is quite probable that, at the outset, the costs of improved water quality will not be matched by the value of associated benefits. Eventually, the value of benefits will rise rapidly until incremental benefits equal incremental costs (Point A). Benefits will exceed costs from Point A to Point B, but the ratio will gradually decrease until the incremental benefits are again equal to incremental costs (Point B). Beyond that point, increments of cost will exceed increments of benefit. Hence, Point B is commonly referred to as the most economically efficient project scale, because this point maximizes benefits in terms of associated costs.

Since the degree of restoration can be directly implied from the derived optimum cost (Point C), a detailed benefit-cost analysis can identify how much restoration is enough. Unfortunately, this proves to be somewhat of an oversimplification. The analysis requires that all benefits be equated to a monetary value, but the intangibles associated with some aspects of maintaining environmental quality do not lend themselves to such a rigorous evaluation. Despite the recognized deficiencies of benefit-cost analysis, application to the extent possible would provide the nation with a better basis upon which to judge how much improvement is enough.

A few of the benefits which can be quantified are:

(1) enhancement of land values;
(2) reduced cost of water treatment for domestic, municipal, and industrial supplies;
(3) enhancement of the fishery resource, both commercial and sport;
(4) enhancement of water-based recreation activities and increased potential for providing water-based recreation opportunities;
(5) minimization of the potential public health hazard; and
(6) an upgrading of the aesthetic appeal of the Lakes and thereby their drawing power with respect to tourists.

Benefits derived from improved water quality continually change with time. For example, demographic and sociological trends such as increased population, leisure time, income, and mobility will put increasing pressure on the Great Lakes as a recreational resource. The problem is com-

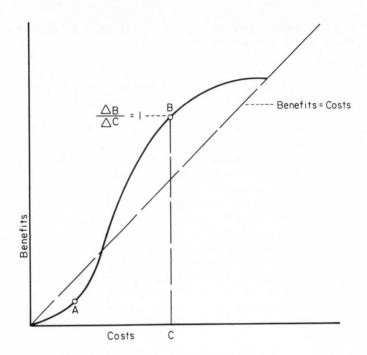

Figure A-1. Benefit-Cost Analysis

pounded by the fact that as population density increases, social pressures arise to place a higher value on recreational opportunities. Therefore, the value to the individual of such opportunities in the future will be greater than the value today. By the year 2020, for example, the projected population in the Lake Erie Basin alone is expected to pass 23 million as compared with 9.8 million in 1960,[9] but the rate of increase in water-based recreation demand is estimated to far exceed this population growth rate.

B Great Lakes Ecology

C. C. Coutant *

In this appendix, the general features of Great Lakes ecology are described and principal disturbances which now affect human activities are indicated. While the foci of ecological considerations are most often organisms, usually fish of importance to commercial or sport fishery interests, there is interaction in both directions between biota and the physical and chemical features referred to as water quality. Biota serve as indicators of water quality; they also contribute to its change. Both water quality and biota are greatly influenced by the physical limnology of the Lakes, as outlined briefly below. For sake of brevity, the discussions avoid consideration of most tributaries. A thorough analysis must consider these many and diverse subsystems, because their contributions of industrial pollutants, pesticides, silts, and other artifacts of human activity cause many of the ecological changes noted in the Lakes. Preparation of this appendix was aided considerably by Mr. Robert Schueler, U.S. Bureau of Commercial Fisheries, Ann Arbor, who provided a number of pertinent reports, some unpublished.

The large size of the Lakes has limited the development of a knowledge of many aspects of their ecology. Considerable information has been amassed, however, on certain facets of Great Lakes limnology, especially in applied areas such as water levels. In other areas of interest to the aquatic ecologist, very little is known. Descriptions of major portions of the biota are extremely rudimentary, for example, plankton and other organisms of the open waters of the Lake centers. Large vessels and sturdier equipment than those in use on smaller lakes are necessary. Without major national efforts on the lakes comparable to naval investments in the oceans, the techniques of oceanography have found slow application until recently. A major concern now is the lack of precise knowledge of past conditions to relate to the apparent changes evident in recent years.

Lake Morphometry

The Great Lakes individually rank among the world's largest. Lake Superior is the largest body of fresh water in the world, occupying 83,000 km^2. It is the deepest of the Great Lakes, and it is the uppermost Lake in the system. Superior discharges approximately 73,700 cfs via St. Mary's River. This volume is derived from the surrounding watershed, which includes a few large rivers and two artificial diversions of Hudson Bay drainage into the north shore of the Lake. There is a high proportion of lake

---

* Currently with the Oak Ridge National Laboratory, Oak Ridge, Tennessee.

area to total basin area, a characteristic common to all of the Great Lakes. This feature tends to reduce the immediate impact on the lakes of nutrients and pollutants derived from tributaries. The level of Lake Superior is maintained near 600.4 feet above sea level by compensating works at Sault St. Marie. There are no major subbasins in Lake Superior, although there are embayments and a major island at the north shore.

Lakes Huron and Michigan rank fifth and sixth in size among the world's lakes. Lake Michigan drains into Lake Huron through the Straits of Mackinac, and the surfaces of these two Lakes have essentially the same elevation, 578.8 feet above sea level. In area, Lake Huron is the second largest of the Great Lakes. It receives water at about 55,000 cfs from Lake Michigan and 73,780 cfs from Lake Superior. Most water flows through the St. Clair River at 177,900 average cfs. This Lake occupies 32 percent (23,000 square miles or 59,510 km^2) of its 72,000-square-mile watershed (including the Lake). The Lake is divided into two principal basins. The main Lake is separated from North Channel and Georgian Bay at the north and northeast by Bruce Peninsula and many islands. The maximum depth, 762 feet, occurs in the northeast portion of the main basin. Lake Huron is second to Lake Erie in the proportion of shallow (less than 100 feet in depth) water. Saginaw Bay, a shallow arm 51 miles long and 26 miles wide at the mouth, is the largest embayment on the west shore. It is fed by the Saginaw River. The predominant bottom material of Lake Huron is clay, although there are local deposits of gravel, sand, and silt.

Lake Michigan occupies 22,400 square miles, or about one-third of its 67,860-square-mile watershed. It is the third largest of the Great Lakes. Two major depressions occur on the Lake, one in the southern end with depths to 564 feet and the other in the northern half where the maximum depth is 923 feet. These depressions are separated by a shallower area with depths of around 270 feet or less, extending out from the vicinity of Milwaukee, Wisconsin. Only 10 percent of the Lake, however, is less than 40 feet deep. A major embayment, Green Bay, lies along the northwest shoreline, separated from the Lake proper by two peninsulas and a number of islands and shoals. Green Bay is relatively shallow, maximum depth 160 feet, and occupies a surface area of 1590 square miles. It has several subembayments which provide ecologically distinct areas.

Lake Erie ranks twelfth in size of lakes of the world and fourth in the Great Lakes. Western Lake Erie receives the waters of Lake Huron which have discharged through the St. Clair River, Lake St. Clair, and the Detroit River at an average flow of 177,600 cfs. Lake Erie discharges into Lake Ontario through the Niagara River. The flow through the Niagara River can vary from about 120,000 to over 300,000 cfs in a week with a mean discharge of about 200,000 cfs. Lake Erie is 241 miles long and has a maximum width of 57 miles. The drainage basin is 32,490 square miles, including 9,930 square miles of water surface, which is almost one-third of the drainage area. Lake Erie is also the shallowest of the Great Lakes, with over 90 percent of its total being under 80 feet in depth.

Lake Erie is naturally divided into three basins. The western basin extends from the southern tip of Grosse Isle to a line connecting the tip of Point Pelee and the tip of Cedar Point. The central basin extends from this line to a line connecting the base of Long Point and the base of Presque Isle. The eastern basin includes the remaining area to the head of the Niagara River. The western basin contains many shoals and islands situated in the eastern portion of the western basin and surrounded by shallow water. East of the islands the Lake deepens to 60 to 78 feet. A shoal extends from the base of Long Point to within 15 miles of the southern shore. East of the shoal there is a depression with a maximum depth of 210 feet.

Most of the western basin has a mud bottom, although extensive areas of sand exist south of the Detroit River and east of Pelee Island. A narrow band of clay follows the Ohio shore, and rock and gravel shoals, which are spawning grounds for many fishes, abound in the island area. A large gravel area exists near the Ohio shore midway between Sandusky and Toledo. The central and eastern basins have predominantly mud bottoms with sand or clay often existing near shore and in bays.

Lake Ontario, although having the smallest area of the St. Lawrence Great Lakes, ranks fourteenth in size among the lakes of the world. It receives the water of Lake Erie after the 37-mile passage through the Niagara River. The St. Lawrence River carries the discharge of Lake Ontario 502 miles to the Atlantic Ocean. The waters of the Niagara make a rapid descent over Niagara Falls and through the rapids above and below the falls. The difference of mean surface level between Lakes Erie and Ontario is approximately 326 feet. The flow through the Niagara River can vary from about 120,000 to over 300,000 cfs in a week, with a mean discharge of about 200,000 cfs. The mean outflow of Lake Ontario is 240,000 cfs. Lake Ontario is 193 miles long and has a maximum width of 53 miles. The drainage basin is 34,800 square miles including 7,600 square miles of water surface.

One of the most important morphological features of Lake Ontario is its depth. The maximum depth of 802 feet is greater than both Lakes Erie and Huron, and the average depth of 283 feet is exceeded only by Lake Superior. Depths less than 20 fathoms occur only very near shore and in the northeast portion of the Lake, near the St. Lawrence River. Lake Ontario has greater percentage of its area deeper than 20 fathoms than do Lakes Michigan, Huron, or Erie. The deepest portion of the Lake is in the southeast. A number of islands and the extensive Bay of Quinte are found in the relatively shallow northeast.

The bedrock of the Great Lakes region consists of undifferentiated pre-Cambrian and sedimentary Paleozoic rocks. The basins themselves have been formed by excavation of the outcrop belts of the less resistant rocks by glacial action. Most of the basin of Lake Superior and part of Georgian Bay of Lake Huron lie in the pre-Cambrian rock of the Canadian Shield. The rest of the bedrock formation of the Great Lakes is of various Paleozoic periods. Silurian rock forms the western and northern shore of Lake Michigan, the islands and peninsula separating Georgian Bay from Lake Huron, the Niagara escarpment, and the southern shore of Lake Ontario. The Devonian shales form part of the basins of Lakes Erie, Huron, and Michigan. Ordovician shales occur along the west shore of Green Bay and in the deeper areas of Georgian Bay. Most of the Lower Peninsula of the State of Michigan is undifferentiated Pennsylvanian and Mississippian rock. Extensive glacial deposits cover most of the bedrock formations in the Great Lakes region except for the Canadian Shield.

Chemistry

The Great Lakes consist of bicarbonate waters and are thus similar to the average freshwaters of the world. Total alkalinity ranges from 46 ppm (as $CaCO_3$) in Lake Superior to 113 ppm in Lake Michigan (Table B-1). The pH ranges from 8.0 to 8.5 for most of the waters, except Lake Superior for which pH is lower. Sulfate concentrations are greater than chlorides in the upper Lakes, and they are almost equal in Lakes Erie and Ontario. The proportions of calcium, magnesium, and sodium in the upper Lakes are about 10:3:1. Potassium usually averages around 1 ppm in all the Lakes. Silica usually fluctuates around 2 to 3 ppm, although only trace amounts of silica occur at times in the highly productive waters of Lake Erie. Concentrations of total phosphorus are low in the upper Lakes and are usually less than 5 ppb in the open waters of Lake Superior. The phosphorus content of water from Lake Erie is about six times greater than that in the other Lakes.

The dissolved-oxygen content of most of the Great Lakes waters is near saturation, even at the greatest depths, and supersaturation is common.

Dissolved-oxygen content in the surface waters may vary considerably, depending on the time of day and the time of year. Diurnal changes can be significant; for example, the percentage saturation of dissolved oxygen increased from nearly saturation in the morning to 35 percent above saturation by evening near Maumee Bay, Lake Erie, in May 1961. During temporary stratification of the western basin of Erie, dissolved oxygen may be seriously depleted. In September 1953, concentrations of dissolved oxygen as low as 0.7 ppm were recorded. During the thermal stratification of the western basin of Lake Erie in 1963, dissolved-oxygen concentrations were as low as 2.6 ppm. Severe oxygen depletion has been observed in the bottom waters of the central basin of Lake Erie during

Table B-1

Average Chemical Characteristics of Great Lakes Waters

Lake	Calcium, ppm	Magnesium, ppm	Potassium, ppm	Sodium, ppm	Total Alkalinity, ppm CaCO$_3$	Chloride, ppm	Sulfate, ppm	Silica, ppm	Phosphorus, ppb	pH	Specific Conductance, micromhos at 18 C
Superior	12.4	2.8	0.6	1.1	46	1.9	3.2	2.1	5	7.4	78.7
Huron	22.6	6.3 [a]	1.0	2.3 [a]	82	7.0	9.7	2.3	10	8.1	168.3
Michigan	31.5	10.4	0.9	3.4	113	6.2	15.5	3.1	13	8.0	225.8
Erie	36.7	8.9	1.4	8.7	95	21.0	21.1	1.5	61	8.3	241.8
Ontario	39.3	9.1 [b]	1.2	10.8	93	23.5	32.4	0.3	—	8.5 [c]	272.3

Source: U.S. Bureau of Commercial Fisheries data, unless designated otherwise. Data based on samples from various depths. (Adapted from Beeton and Chandler, 1964.)

[a] Ayers et al., 1956.
[b] Leverin, 1947 (average from Toronto intake).
[c] New York State Department of Health, 1958.

periods of thermal stratification every year since 1958. Critically low dis-solved oxygen has not been reported to date in the eastern basin.

Laboratory and field experiments have shown that while the biochemi-cal-oxygen-demand (BOD) of Lake Erie water is insufficient to deplete the hypolimnion of dissolved oxygen, the sediments have a sufficiently high oxygen demand to explain the low dissolved-oxygen concentrations during stratification. A very rapid uptake of dissolved oxygen occurs when a small amount of sediment is mixed with oxygenated water. This im-mediate oxygen demand is probably chemical, whereas a continued gradual uptake of oxygen is probably biological. The high-immediate-oxygen-demand sediments have the greatest organic content.

Widespread oxygen depletion, present in Lake Erie, does not occur in the other Lakes, although there are local exceptions. The central basin of Lake Erie is relatively shallow, and therefore, the thermocline over a large area of the basin is 10 feet or less from the bottom. Only near shore in the other Lakes does thermal stratification occur this near the bottom. Even if sediments have a high oxygen demand, the reservoir of oxygen in a hypolimnion several hundred feet thick is too great for the sediments to materially reduce it during the few months when stratifica-tion occurs.

Current Patterns

Present evidence indicates that the currents in most of the Lakes are variable and respond rather quickly to wind changes. An attempt has not been made to study the general circulation in all areas of Lake Superior. The published (Ruschmeyer et al., 1958; Beeton et al., 1959) and un-published data show, however, that certain persistent currents occur. A well-defined littoral current flows from west to east along the south shore. This littoral current may be part of a general counterclockwise circulation of the entire Lake.

Patterns of circulation in Lake Huron were studied in 1954 (Ayers et al., 1956). Two parent water masses, from Lakes Michigan and Superior, and a mixture of the two, Lake Huron, were present. Lake Superior water could be followed for only short distances, horizontally or vertically. Lake Michigan and mixed Lake Huron water were both widespread on the surface. At greater depths, Lake Huron water was present on both sides of the Lake, but Lake Michigan water was present only on the west side. Both masses were traceable into the southern end of the Lake.

Surface water basically circulated counterclockwise in the upper and central portions of the Lake. Near the south end of the Lake the surface water seemed to meander toward the outlet from the northeast. Data sug-gested that surface circulation is influenced by winds of the preceding 12 days. Little is known of subsurface currents in Lake Huron.

Although sinking and upwellings did occur during 1954, the thermocline was generally an effective barrier to complete vertical circulation. Some major sinkings did appear to penetrate the thermocline and buoy it up. Upwellings usually occurred near shore as a result of offshore winds pushing warm upper layers into the open lake.

During spring and fall, a thermal bar, or mixing zone between waters less than 4 C and waters greater than 4 C, constitutes a barrier to extensive offshore-onshore movement of water. This has also been observed in other lakes. The thermal bar, when it is close to shore in spring, probably limits movement of runoff (including pollutants) from inshore to offshore areas. Sampling done close to shore in the spring and early summer would not be representative of the open lake (Rogers, 1965).

In shallow Saginaw Bay, circulation is highly variable, depending both on local winds and the stronger Lake Huron circulation. However, the prevailing circulation is counterclockwise; Lake Huron water enters from the northeast and flows along the bay's north shore; the Saginaw River enters Lake Huron via the south shore of Saginaw Bay (Beeton, 1958; Johnson, 1958; Beeton et al., 1967). Results of drift card studies in Georgian Bay suggest an upwelling on the west shore and west to east movement of surface water (Fry, 1956).

Knowledge of the currents of Lake Michigan has increased considerably within the past 10 years. Most of the studies have been concerned primarily with surface currents; subsurface water movements and their relation to the surface remain relatively little known. Furthermore, most observations on surface currents have not extended over long enough periods to support conclusions as to prevailing seasonal patterns. New studies with autmatic current meter systems should provide insight into the complexities of water movements in Lake Michigan.

The nonperiodic horizontal circulation of the Lake is an integration of the effects of generating agents—wind and density differences (as modified by morphology of the basin), the rotation of the earth, and hydraulic currents. At times, some large eddies develop, especially in the southern and northern areas of the Lake. A general west-to-east drift of surface water is usually present and the current along the eastern shore is predominantly northbound. The outflow through the Straits of Mackinac probably lends some stability to this current. The normal current from Lake Michigan to Lake Huron has occasionally been reversed during intense storms with strong easterly winds.

An outstanding feature of the water movements in Green Bay off Lake Michigan is the high degree of irregularity in direction and velocity, believed to be governed mainly by wind and barometric pressure. Flow of water into Green Bay from rivers is believed to be of minor importance in the major water movements except during spring runoff. Movement of Lake Michigan water into Green Bay is characterized more by surges than by a regular movement. Surges into Green Bay result primarily from seiche action set in motion by wind and pressure changes over Lake Michigan. The resultant currents in Green Bay cause a considerable mixing. In the northern passages, the sequence of inflow, mixing, and outflow result in a great amount of water exchange between the Bay and the Lake. Evidence of a high degree of exchange in the northern area is found in the extension of relatively clear, Lake Michigan water into the green-colored water produced by dense phytoplankton growth characteristic of the remainder of the Bay. Definite lines of demarcation cannot be made on this basis, however, because of mixing of water masses. Clear lake water is sometimes observed in the Sturgeon Bay area, but here a sharp line of demarcation is usually present between the two types of water. This condition indicates that little mixing occurs before the lake water is returned with an outgoing surge through the canal.

In addition to water movements propagated by currents and water level changes in Lake Michigan, the water in the Bay itself is subject to indigenous seiches and currents caused by local conditions. The systems operating simultaneously in the Lake and Bay result in extremely complex and irregular water movements. The water level in Green Bay is subject to almost continuous change. A change of a foot an hour is not uncommon, and, occasionally, a drop of several feet in the southern end of the bay strands fishing boats in shallow harbors.

A general west to ease direction of currents in Lake Erie is evident, which is caused by the predominantly westerly winds along the major axis of the Lake and the large inflow at the western end and large outflow at the eastern end. In the western basin, a reversal in wind direction can cause the surface current to be completely reversed. The major portion of the Detroit River flow usually does not spread out over the entire western basin, since after it enters the Lake, it flows to the north shore and enters the central basin between Pelee Point and Pelee Island. Polluted waters from the west side of the Detroit, Maumee, and Raisin Rivers usually flow through the southern part of the western basin and into the central basin between Pelee and Kelleys Islands and Kelleys Island and Marblehead Peninsula. The usual flow pattern in the central basin is dominated by a prevailing west-to-east current along the Ohio shore. River water tends to flow out on the lake surface in summer and sink to the bottom in winter owing to thermal differences between lake and river water. Little information is available on currents in the eastern basin, but these probably are dominated by the influence of the Niagara River. Studies on the subsurface currents of Lake Erie have not been completed. Present evidence indicates that the cooler waters of the Detroit River sink below the surface after the Lake has warmed.

Lake Ontario also has a general west-to-east direction of surface currents caused by the same factors that operate in Lake Erie. The predominant easterly flow is along the New York shore, with a weaker return flow along the northern shore. This westerly flow extends for about two-thirds the distance of the Lake. The Niagara River flow is strongly developed eastwardly and a counterclockwise circular current pattern probably exists during periods of thermal stratification in the western portion of the Lake. This results in a long retention time for pollutants discharged into this area. After fall overturn, the winds shifts more northerly; the surface current in the western end is eastward and a westward bottom current is developed. This net movement of surface water from west to east results in upwelling in the western part and a flushing of any buildup of pollutants. Little information is available on currents in the extreme northeastern portion of the basin, but these are undoubtedly dominated by the influence of the St. Lawrence River. Recent studies using infrared imagery have identified heretofore unknown surface circulation patterns of major and minor significance. Analysis of this work is just beginning.

Thermal Patterns

All of the Lakes exhibit some degree of thermal stratification during the warmer months. They probably mix deeply throughout most of the winter and spring, since solid ice sheets are mostly limited to such sheltered areas as embayments, channels, among islands, and along shore. Ice in the main lakes usually occurs as floes. The Lakes differ chiefly in the rate at which they warm and in the stability of the thermal stratification.

The effect of deep winter mixing is apparent in Lake Superior where homothermous water around 2 C occurs to depths of 600 feet (Beeton et al., 1959). Lake Superior is much colder than the other Lakes and usually does not exhibit any well-defined stratification until mid-July. The lower limit of the epilimnion is around 45 feet. Thermal stratification is not uniform from area to area, and the metalimnion is usually poorly developed.

In general, Lake Huron undergoes the same annual temperature cycle observed in most other freshwater lakes of the temperate zone. Specifically, the deep water remains near the temperature of maximum density (4 C or ca 39 F) throughout the year, whereas surface and shallow waters undergo considerable thermal change through the seasons (Millar, 1952). In the spring, surface water gradually warms from 1 C (34 F) to 4 C until the lake proper is vertically homothermous. Shallow water may warm more rapidly, depending on local conditions. Temporary thermal stratification may occur in early June.

During July and August, a well-defined and persistent thermal stratification is established. The upper layer (epilimnion) is fairly homothermous (16 to 20 C) and extends to a depth of 50 feet (Hachey, 1952). Water above 20 C (68 F) may occur particularly near shorelines. The thermocline is present over all the open lake except at the extreme ends where inlet and outlet currents cause appreciable mixing.

A cooler, more turbulent atmosphere in the autumn creates considerable reduction in temperature of epilimnetic waters, eventually resulting in circulation of the entire water column as a 4 C mass. Few data are available on autumn cooling in Lake Huron, and the cycle is assumed to be similar to that in Lake Michigan. During gradual warming of Lake Michigan in the spring, the surface waters, which are around 1 C (34 F) during the winter, attain 4 C (39 F), and the main body of the lake is homothermous by mid-May. Warming progresses somewhat faster along the shore, in bays, and around islands, and temperatures may be 3 to 4 C higher in these areas than in the open lake. Some thermal stratification may occur by early June, but it usually is transitory.

Persistent thermal stratification is established by late June. The upper warm-water layer (epilimnion) extends to a depth of about 45 feet. Temperatures decrease quite rapidly below the epilimnion in the metalimnion and are around 6 to 7 C (43 to 45 F) at a depth of 75 feet. This general thermal structure does not change appreciably throughout the summer, except for some increase in the depth of the epilimnion due to continued warming and mixing by strong winds. Occasionally, the cold bottom waters are brought close to or to the surface along the shores. This upwelling occurs when strong winds have shifted the warm surface waters away from the shore.

The epilimnetic waters undergo considerable cooling in September and October, and by the end of October, surface temperatures are around 10 to 13 C (50 to 55 F). The thermocline may be found at depths of 250 feet during this period because of the decreased resistance to mixing and stronger winds during the fall. Slightly higher temperatures occur in the bottom waters, indicating some mixing of the deep waters with the warm epilimnetic waters. In fact, any warming of the deeper bottom waters is noticeable only during late fall. The shallow shore waters cool somewhat faster than the open lake, and differences of 4 to 5 C (39 to 42 F) may occur.

Cooling continues throughout the winter and into early spring. Open lake waters may be homothermous at around 3 C (37 F) in March and April, while waters in shallower areas may be homothermous at less than 1 C (34 F).

The thermal cycle of Green Bay is somewhat different from that of Lake Michigan proper, because of the extensive areas of shallow water. These shallow areas change temperature much more rapidly than the open lake and are more noticeably influenced by fluctuations in air temperatures. Temperatures in the shallow waters of southern Green Bay usually have risen by 10 C (52 F) by early May, and it is only during this warming period that transitory thermal stratification occurs. Maximum temperatures, around 21 C (70 F), are attained under homothermous conditions in July. Rapid cooling occurs in late August and in September.

The waters in the deeper areas of Green Bay, especially those near the channels connecting the Bay and the Lake, do not warm as rapidly as the shallow waters. The exchange of bay and lake waters in this area undoubtedly is an important factor. These waters usually are well stratified by mid-June. Some warming of the deeper waters occurs, since temperatures are around 7 to 8 C (44 to 46 F) at 100 feet in July.

The waters of Lake Erie undergo considerable thermal change seasonally. During severe winters, 95 percent of the surface may be ice covered. Gradual warming begins in March or April and continues through the spring. Warming progresses somewhat faster along the shore and around islands, and may be 2 to 3 C (4 to 6 F) higher in these areas than in the open lake.

The western basin is usually homothermous, but prolonged periods of hot, calm weather can cause temporary thermal stratification, owing to warming of the surface waters, of considerable importance to the biota. The most recent occurrence of such stratification was at the end of June 1963, after 4 consecutive days when the daytime temperature was above 32 C (90 F) and the winds were light and variable. The maximum thermal gradient observed was approximately 1 C (2 F) per foot, and a maximum temperature difference between the surface and bottom water of 6.5 C (11.7 F) was found. Thermal stratification in the central basin is more stable and the thermal gradient in the thermocline more pronounced. Areas where the depth is greater than 40 feet are usually well stratified by the beginning of July every year, although transitory stratification may occur during the spring. The thermal gradient is usually steep and may be as great as 7.3 C (13.1 F) per foot. Surface water temperature rarely exceeds 26 C (79 F) except in local areas during short periods. Stratification in the deeper areas of the central basin may persist until at least the end of September.

Stratification in the deeper areas of the eastern basin starts in June and continues until October or November. The hypolimnion in the deep hole starts warming in late summer and early fall and reaches a maximum temperature of approximately 10 C (50 F). The rate of temperature change with depth is not as great in the deeper water of Lake Erie, but differences of almost 17 C (31 F) may exist between the surface and bottom water.

Lake Ontario also undergoes considerable thermal change seasonally. Lake Ontario is unique among the Great Lakes in that ice conditions during the winter do not seriously hamper shipping. It is considered unlikely that more than 60 percent of Lake Ontario would be ice covered except in the most severe winters. This is probably due to the depth of the basin, its southerly latitude, and faster currents than are present in the other Lakes. In late winter, the Lake is thermally the most homogenous, with the water in the western end and over the deepest part of the lake being slightly warmer than water in the rest of the Lake. Gradual warming begins in April and continues through the spring. Warming progresses somewhat faster along the shore, and may be 2 C (3.6 F) higher than in the open lake.

By June the surface water near shore is 10 to 14 C (50 to 57 F) and is about 10 meters thick. On the southern shore, considerably more warming is experienced and 20 C (68 F) water may be found near the mouth of the Niagara. The epilimnion becomes warmer as the summer progresses, although the thermocline does not deepen rapidly. Surface temperatures reach a maximum in August, and the thermocline begins accelerated deepening. In portions of the eastern basin, conditions may be homothermous to 100 feet in August, probably because of mixing caused by an active local current pattern. Differences as great as 23 C (41 F) between the surface and bottom water may occur in the deeper waters of Lake Ontario where the bottom waters do not warm above 4 C (39 F). Cooling of the surface waters occurs concurrently with the deepening of the thermocline. By late November the thermocline is more than 60 meters deep and there is less than 3 C difference between the temperature of the epilimnion and hypolimnion.

Aquatic Life

Limnoplankton

There is a remarkable dearth of information on the plankton of the Great Lakes, despite the importance of this community for primary production and for nuisance accumulations. In general, the plankton is typical of that in large, deep lakes. Lake Superior sustains a very sparse plankton and is known for its generally clear, transparent water. Secchi disk readings in excess of 50 feet are not uncommon. Recent siltation derived from production of taconite has reduced this clarity, however. Attempts to study primary productivity of Lake Superior were hampered by the need for extensive artificial concentration of samples to achieve measurable production (Putnam and Olson, 1961). Diatoms predominate the phytoplankton, while copepods predominate in the zooplankton.

Little attention has been given the plankton of Lake Huron, and published studies of these important organisms are, for the most part, qualitative. The diatoms (Bacillariacceae) have been reported as the dominant plankters throughout the year (Davis, 1966). The most abundant forms of diatoms have been *Fragilaria, Tabellaria,* and *Cyclotella. Asterionella* is also common, but not as abundant as the other three genera. Zooplankton may, at times, equal the diatoms in biomass, although no quantitative information is available. Rotifers and protozoans, although apparently more numerous, probably compose less bulk than planktonic crustaceans. Of the latter, copepods seem dominant over cladocerans. *Diaptomus sicilis, D. ashlandi, D. minutis, D. oregonenis,* and *Senecella calanoides* are the more common forms in the middle and upper layers of the Lake (Robertson, 1966). *Limnocalanus macrurus* is probably an important deep-water form.

Estimates of plankton abundance in Lake Huron have not yet been published. More quantitative information is needed since these organisms no doubt comprise the bulk of basic organic production. The Great Lakes Institute, University of Toronto, has made extensive quantitative collections of zooplankton throughout Lake Huron. Preliminary analyses suggest that standing crop of zooplankters is greater in the southern half of the Lake (Great Lakes Institute, 1964).

In Lake Michigan, diatoms are the most important constituents of the plankton, although zooplankton may occasionally equal the diatoms in biomass and *Dinobryon* is especially abundant at times. There is few data on Green Bay. The more abundant diatom genera are *Asterionella, Cyclotella, Fragilaria, Melosira, Synedra,* and *Tabellaria.* Copepods probably make up the bulk of the zooplankton, although protozoans may be more numerous. Rotifers are usually plentiful and cladocerans are very abundant in the summer. The coldwater copepod *Limnocalanus macrurus* is the important zooplankter in the deep waters. Several copepods (*Cyclops bicuspidatus, Diaptomus ashlandi, D. minutis, D. oregonensis,* and *D. sicilis*) occur in the upper strata of the Lake. The dominant cladoceran species (*Daphnia galeata mendotae, D. retrocurva,* and *Bosmina longirostris*) are also found in the warm epilimnetic waters.

Little is known of the abundance of plankton. The spring pulse consists almost entirely of diatoms. Populations of blue-green and green algae increase somewhat during the summer and contribute to the fall pulse, although diatoms remain dominant. The abundance of plankton varies considerably throughout the Lake. Comparison of plankton data from the National Water Quality Network stations at Gary, Indiana, and Milwaukee, Wisconsin, shows considerable differences between these two localities for the period July, 1960, to July, 1961. The average phytoplankton count was 975 and 1,914 plankters per milliliter at Milwaukee and at Gary, respectively. Local differences in the relative importance of the major diatom species at Gary and Milwaukee also are apparent. Sampling by the Bureau of Commercial Fisheries in 1960 yielded further evidence of wide variability between inshore stations such as Gary and Milwaukee and the open lake. Plankton counts in open-lake samples ranged from about 450 to 12,000 plankters per milliliter and averaged around 4,500 per milliliter.

The vertical distribution of copepods and cladocerans changes throughout the day. All the species which have been studied migrate toward, and attain their greatest numbers at, the surface late in the day, apparently in response to diurnal changes in light intensity. Thermal conditions evidently interact with and modify the influence of light, since certain species will not migrate through a steep thermal gradient in the metalimnion.

Comparison of the results of various studies of phytoplankton dating back to 1872 shows that the diatom species dominant 90 years ago have maintained their importance. The relative abundance and occurrence of individual species give no evidence of change in the phytoplankton such as would be expected with advanced eutrophication.

The best information of change of plankton abundance probably comes from 33 years of plankton data from the Chicago water intake, which show an average increase of 13 organisms per milliliter per year in the standing crop of the total plankton. It should be recognized, however, that most of the past work on plankton has been in the extreme southern end of the Lake, which may reflect only local conditions.

Two changes in the species composition of the zooplankton may be of some consequence for indicating increased eutrophication of Lake Michigan. Apparently the cladoceran, *Bosmina longirostris,* has replaced *B. coregoni.* A similar change occurred in Lake Zurich, Switzerland, when it was undergoing substantial changes toward eutrophy. *Bosmina coregoni* was the most abundant cladoceran in Lake Michigan in 1887 to 1888 and 1926 to 1927, and *B. longirostris* was considered rare. By 1954, *B. longirostris* had replaced *B. coregoni,* and the latter species is seldom found in plankton samples. Also, *Diaptomus oregonensis* was not reported by earlier investigators, but in recent years it has been present in most plankton samples and it is the dominant diaptomid at times.

Plankton has received the greatest attention in Lake Erie, and new data are being obtained rapidly in this Lake. Diatoms usually comprise 75 percent of the phytoplankton. The more abundant phytoplankton genera are *Fragilaria, Melosira, Synedra, Stephanodiscus, Anabaena,* and *Microcystis.* Two periods of peak plankton abundance occur yearly, one in the spring and one in the fall. The spring pulse consists almost entirely of diatoms. Populations of blue-green and green algae build up during August and September and contribute to the fall pulse, although diatoms are still dominant. These pulses are very important in the primary productivity of the Lake. In 1942 the population of phytoplankton during pulses made up 83 percent of the year's standing crop. There is a great deal of horizontal variability in the plankton of Lake Erie and probably of the other lakes as well. Sampling at a given station repeatedly for four years has shown that different water masses were probably sampled at each visit (Davis, 1954).

During the past 26 years, a consistent increase had been noted in the quantity of phytoplankton at the Cleveland water intake and at other nearshore locations. The peak abundance of phytoplankton during the spring and fall has also risen sharply, and the periods of peak abundance now last longer than in the past. *Asterionella* was the dominant diatom in the spring in earlier years; *Melosira* is now dominant. *Synedra* dominated the fall pulse in the 1920s, but it was replaced by *Melosira,* and more recently *Fragilaria* and the blue-green alga, *Anabaena,* have been important. These changes suggest increased eutrophy.

Copepods, especially *Cyclops bicuspidatus, Diaptomus minutis, D. sicilis, D. ashlandi,* and *D. oregonensis,* make up the bulk of the zooplankton in Lake Erie, although protozoans are more numerous. Cladocerans and rotifers are very abundant in summer. The large zooplankters are usually abundant in summer and the smaller ones abundant in spring and fall.

Important changes have taken place in the zooplankton population of Lake Erie. Copepods and especially cladocerans have shown a marked increase in abundance since 1939. The copepod, *Diaptomus siciloides,* which occurred incidentally in 1929 and 1930, is now one of the two most abundant diaptomids.

Recent sampling in Lake Ontario revealed a change in phytoplankton composition indicative of nutrient enrichment. A 1965 survey showed that the phytoplankton population varied from 50 to 3600 organisms per milliliter. Although these figures are considered to be moderate for biological activity, the dominant alga in the spring pulse (May) was *Scenedesmus,* and in July and September was *Chlamydomonas.* Both genera are indicators of nutrient enrichment and are not found in any other of the Great Lakes except Lake Erie. In mid-July a bloom of the blue-green alga, *Anabaena,* occurred. Its intensity was recorded at 10,000 organisms per milliliter, and indicates eutrophic conditions.

Data accumulated at the City of Toronto Water Filtration Plant indicate that the phytoplankton doubled from 1923 to 1954. This period was characterized by a well-defined spring maximum and a well-defined winter minimum. Fall maxima were inconsistent and lower than the spring maxima. The summer months were characterized by short, lesser pulses, a pulse being defined as a plankton count at least two times the annual mean. During the entire period diatoms were dominant.

There was a change, however, in dominance among the diatoms during the spring pulses. *Asterionella* was the dominant genus until 1937. After 1938, *Melosira* became more prominent and increased in importance during the succeeding vernal pulses. *Cyclotella* increased in numbers after 1941 and was the dominant genus in 1950, 1952, and 1954.

During the fall of nearly every year, August to October, *Fragilaria* was dominant. However, its abundance was not great enough to constitute a pulse. *Tabellaria* occasionally increased in numbers at this time. Both the summer and winter seasons were generally characterized by low levels of a population of mixed diatoms. Among the blue-green algae, *Anabaena* and *Oscillatoria* were occasionally present. The flagellates were represented by *Dinobryon* which occurred frequently, with sporadic appearance by *Synura* and *Mallomonas.*

Although *Cladophora* is not a plankter, but rather a periphyton (attached) organism, it is an alga that had reached nuisance proportions in Lake Ontario by the 1930s. In a 1963 study by Neil and Owen, the distribution of *Cladophora* was found to be concentrated on the northern shore of Lake Ontario from the south shore of Prince Edward County to the Niagara River. A 1965 survey showed *Cladophora* to be distributed on all shores of Lake Ontario wherever suitable substrate occurred. It is now a major nuisance throughout the Lake, where it creates dense mats of growth on rocky substrates and breaks loose in streams to dog water intakes and accumulates in rotting piles and windrows along beaches and in sheltered bays. Its recent proliferation is one outstanding feature of increased lake eutrophication. Experimental studies indicate that areas devoid of this alga can produce sizable growths on application of phosphorus in excess of that normally available (Neil and Owen, 1964).

Benthos (Bottom Organisms)

The deep water bottom fauna of all of the deep Great Lakes is apparently similar in composition. It is dominated by amphipods (*Pontoporeia affinis*) and mysids (*Mysis relicta*) which are very important in the forage base for fishes such as coregonids, smelt, alewives, and sulpins. Although primarily benthic, individuals of both of these crustacean species often migrate at night to the lake surface, or at least, to the thermocline (Beeton, 1960). The amphipods, which contributed about 70 percent of the volume in Lake Michigan, may have a zone of maximum density near depths of 120 feet according to results of a study in South Bay of Lake Huron (Cooper, 1962). Other important profundal forms numerically abundant are oligochaetes, sphaeriid clams (mostly *Pisidium* and *Sphaerium*), and midge-fly larvae (tendipedids), of the *Spaniotoma* group in that order (Teter, 1960).

The quality of benthic fauna changes in harbors and other inshore areas: oligochaetes, often a biological indicator of enriched or polluted habitat, are dominant both in bulk and numbers. *Limnodrilus hoffmeisteri,* a tubificid, is probably the most common, at least of the large oligochaetes. In Saginaw Bay, off Lake Huron, the distribution of *L. hoffmeisteri* correlates well with the known flow of the river out of the Bay (Brinkhurst 1967). This may demonstrate the presence of a polluting inflow, but observations on another bay with unpolluted inflow are required for comparison. Experts generally agree that sediment quality in Saginaw Bay may be of significant influence in such a distribution, but the specific characteristics of the sediment (for example, type of food materials) responsible have not yet been defined.

Surveys of the bottom fauna of Green Bay (Lake Michigan) have shown that pollution-tolerant forms are dominant in southern Green Bay, especially in the area where the Fox River flows into the Bay. Pollution-tolerant forms also are very abundant off the mouth of the Oconto River. Limited sampling in the part of the Bay where it is connected to Lake Michigan indicates that the fauna in this area is similar to that of the open lake. In Lake Ontario, surveys of Toronto Harbor indicate disturbances due to pollution that are similar to those noted above.

In relatively remote, pollution-free inshore areas, organisms common to smaller inland lakes are found, such as leeches, various midges, snails, caddisflies, mayflies, and amphipods (*Gammarus* and *Hyallela*). Quantity of these benthic forms varies between inshore and offshore areas, and among the Lakes: studies in 1965 indicate that average density is six times greater in Saginaw Bay than in deep water (Schuytema and Powers, 1966). In the same studies, all Lake Huron samples (Georgian Bay excluded) average 2,100 organisms per square meter, about half the average computed from similar sampling in Lake Michigan.

Because of its shallowness, Lake Erie is distinct among the Great Lakes in both its normal bottom fauna, and in its problems related to this community of organisms. It also has been the most extensively studied.

The bottom fauna of the western basin is composed principally of Oligochaeta, Tendipedidae, Sphaeriidae, and Gastropoda. Organisms more abundant near the principal sources of pollution (Maumee, Raisin, and Detroit Rivers) are: Tubificidae (most *Limnodrilus* spp.); larvae of a tendipedie, *Procladius* sp.; the fingernail clam, *Sphaerium transversum;* and the snail, *Valvata sincera*. The polychaete worm, *Manayunkia speciosa,* is very abundant at the Detroit River mouth but apparently absent at the Maumee River mouth. Pollution-intolerant organisms such as amphipods, mayfly nymphs, and caddisfly larvae are scarce near the mouths of rivers.

In general, the macrobenthos of the central basin is sparse and is composed mainly of midgefly larvae and oligochaetes. The worms are almost entirely of the families Tubificidae and Naididae. The most common tubificid is *Peloscolex ferox*.

The fauna of the deeper eastern basin is more nearly like that of the upper Lakes, and is composed of *Pontoporeia affinis, Mysis relicta,* deepwater species of Tendipedidae, and among others, worms of the family Lumbriculidae (*Stylodrilus heringianus*).

Major changes have recently occurred in the bottom fauna of western Lake Erie. The changes are pollution related and are detrimental to the commercial and recreational use of the Lake. Prior to 1953 the population of mayfly larvae in the island region averaged around 400 per square meter of lake bottom. A prolonged period of very calm weather in the summer of 1953 resulted in thermal stratification that was accompanied by severe oxygen depletion in the bottom waters. Few live mayfly larvae and numerous dead ones could be found at that time. The mayflies recovered rapidly in 1954 to their former abundance, but in 1957 the Bureau of Commercial Fisheries found only 39 nymphs per square meter. In 1959, stations studied in 1954 were revisited and an average of 11 nymphs per square meter was found. One of these stations, where over 9,000 nymphs per square meter were collected in 1954, had only 5 per square meter in 1959. Data for the island region show that oligochaetes increased from 12 per square meter in 1929 to 299 per square meter in 1957. Caddisfly larvae were formerly abundant, but averaged less than 1 per square meter in 1957.

Important changes have taken place in the species composition of the benthos in the area west of the islands. Between 1930 and 1961, there was a ninefold increase in Oligochaeta, a fourfold increase in Tendipedidae, a twofold increase in Sphaeriidae, a sixfold increase in Gastropoda, and a reduction of Hexagenia to less than one percent of the former abundance.

Limited data from the central basin for 1929 to 1930 and 1957 and 1959 collected from the same area show that the large midge larvae of *Tendipes plumosus* has replaced mayfly nymphs as the dominant larger form. Oligochaetes and fingernail clams showed an increase over the 1929 to 1930 samples. Samples taken after a period of low dissolved-oxygen concentrations in 1959 showed that all organisms except nematodes had decreased in abundance.

Cladophora, a filamentous, green, benthic alga, grows in the inshore areas of all of the Lakes, sometimes to nuisance proportions. Its presence seems mainly dependent on suitable substrate for attachment, water movement, adequate light, and nutrients in excess of those normally available.

Fish

The fish fauna of the Great Lakes and tributaries includes representatives of most families of North American fishes. Species distribution has been determined largely by prehistoric patterns of glacial meltwater flow (which provided avenues of colonization not now available) and by recent introductions, both intentional and inadvertent, by man. The salmonid fishes dominated the faunas of all lakes prior to white man, and in Lake Superior no other group has yet been greatly abundant. Lake trout (*Salvelinus namaycush*), lake whitefish (*Coregonus clupeaformis*), and Cisco or lake herring (*C. artedii*) dominated commercial catches in the last half of the nineteenth century, during which time there was no evidence of population decline in the upper Lakes. Native species included a wide variety of small fishes—various cyprinids, cottids, sticklebacks, trout, perch —that had no commercial value but were significant portions of the balanced fauna. Embayments such as Saginaw Bay off Lake Huron produced large quantities of suckers, yellow perch (*Perca flavescens*), and walleye (*Stizostedion vitreum vitreum*) indicating a somewhat different fauna associated with shallower, warmer areas.

Two significant fauna changes were recorded in the commercial landings prior to 1900. One was the appearance of carp in the catch following its introduction into the United States in 1874. Production in Lake Huron rose from zero in 1898 to over 1 million pounds by 1917. The lake sturgeon catch which accounted for over 500,000 pounds in 1889 was insignificant by 1909. This decline is attributed to the intensive effort to remove sturgeon from areas where they damaged gear fished for other species. Since sturgeon was of little commercial signficance at the time, the catch was often discarded or left on the bank. Because of their slow growth and late maturity, the species was soon reduced to insignificance for commercial production, and probably for the fish fauna.

Major changes occurred in the fish faunas of the upper Lakes, especially during the period 1930 to 1960, which resulted from a number of possible factors including sea lamprey predation, instances of overfishing, and the spectacular increase in abundance of alewives.

Relatively few changes were recorded in species composition and total landings of the commercial fishery in the upper Lakes (Huron and Superior) until the late 1930s. At that time, predation by the sea lamprey, first recorded in Lake Huron in the 1930s, began to be reflected in landings of lake trout and whitefish. The United States lake trout catch dropped from almost 2.2 million pounds in 1932 to less than 500 pounds in 1949. Whitefish landings, although typically more erratic than lake trout, appeared to have declined at about the same time, dropping from 4.1 million pounds in 1932 to 0.09 million pounds in 1942.

The collapse of the whitefish population may have been hastened by use of the deep trap net in Lake Huron starting in 1928. This gear, first developed on Lake Ontario, was particularly efficient for capturing whitefish, and its use became widespread on Lake Huron during the early 1930s (Van Oosten et al., 1946). In 1935, restrictions were imposed that prohibited setting traps in water deeper than 80 feet, thereby effectively eliminating the use of this gear for whitefish. However, whitefish landings continued to decline after 1935 as lamprey predation further depleted stocks. A brief upturn in landings was recorded from 1946 to 1949 based on the very successful 1943 year class, but since then the catch has not exceeded 0.4 million pounds.

Walleye production in Saginaw Bay fluctuated but without a long term trend until the early 1940s. After 1943, production there began a steady decline reaching a low 5-year average in 1955 to 1959. The only variation from this progressive decline occurred in 1946 when landings rose slightly as a result of the very strong 1943-year class becoming available to the fishery.

Several factors have been associated with the low level of walleye abundance reached by the end of the period. Industrial pollution in Saginaw Bay has been suggested. It has also been noted that the timing of the walleye decline is quite similar to that of the lake trout and whitefish, indicating that the sea lamprey may have contributed to the collapse of the walleye population. Although observations are not available on the incidence of scarring, the seasonal movements of walleye into deeper water in late summer when parasitic-phase lampreys are moving toward shore provides additional evidence that lamprey predation may have been a significant causal factor (Hile and Buettner, 1959). Four major species, carp, catfish, chubs, and alewife, exhibited above average abundance after 1940, although in the case of the chubs, this may be an apparent, rather than a real increase, owing to greater fishing effort.

The present commercial fishery in Lake Huron appears to be dominated by the alewife. Exploratory trawl fishing by the Bureau of Commercial Fisheries in 1965 indicated that alewife was by far the most abundant species in both Saginaw Bay and the open lake (Bureau of Commercial Fisheries, 1965). Carp, smelt, and chubs were the only other species taken in significant numbers. The same species predominated catches of a similar cruise in 1966, although suckers and yellow perch were also significant. Carp accounted for over 50 percent of the lower bay catches (Bureau of Commercial Fisheries, 1966).

The first alewife specimen was recorded from Lake Huron in 1933, although they were undoubtedly present earlier (Miller, 1956). It is believed that the alewife gained access to Lake Huron from Lake Ontario through the Welland Canal and Lake Erie, although there has been speculation that the Trent River system provided direct access from Ontario. A buildup in alewife abundance was not noted until the early 1950s when alewife catches increased markedly in experimental pound nets around 1953 and 1954. The rapid buildup of alewives appears to be responsible for the decline in abundance and production of the lake herring in Saginaw after 1952, although the causal relationship is not clear (Miller, 1956). The buildup of alewife since 1953 probably reached a peak in 1964. The future status of the alewife in Lake Huron is uncertain, but a decline in abundance from 1964 levels is expected. The rate of decrease is likely to be considerably less than in Lake Michigan because lamprey-control activities on Lake Huron have not proceeded to a stage where predator species such as lake trout and chinook and coho salmon can be reestablished to utilize a portion of the alewife population. In addition, the trawl and pound net fisheries of Lake Michigan have taken large quantities of alewife for commercial uses and such fisheries do not exist on Lake Huron.

In Lake Michigan there appear to be many discrete fish stocks, localized in area. This may also be true of the upper Lakes. The following depth distribution has been identified by the Bureau of Commercial Fisheries:

Inshore and shallow: Carp, sturgeon, yellow perch, and walleyes
Shallow to intermediate: Lake herring, lake whitefish, and smelt
Deepwater: Chubs, lake trout (young are shallow to intermediate)
All depths: Alewife.

Although the total annual commercial catch has not fluctuated widely from an average of 26 million pounds, the abundance of each of the eleven major species (which together average 98 percent of the catch) has varied greatly. Of the eight native species, the catch and abundance of five (sturgeon, lake trout, suckers, whitefish, and lake herring) have reached all-time lows in recent years, and a sixth (the walleye) has declined sharply since the period 1955 to 1959. Yellow perch and chubs are the only native species of major importance that have maintained or increased their abundance. Three exotic species (carp, smelt, and alewife), all of low value, have become abundant in the Lake. Together they have accounted for about one-third of the commercial catch in recent years, which has compensated for declines in the six native species.

The causes for the decline of six native species are varied. Large sturgeon were of little commercial value but they damaged gear fished principally for whitefish. Thus, they were fished heavily to remove them from the grounds, and they were soon reduced to insignificance.

The sharp decline since the 1940s in the abundance and catch of lake trout, suckers, and whitefish is attributed primarily to sea lamprey predation. Because the deeper areas inhabited by lake trout were also the preferred range of the sea lamprey, the lake trout was hardest hit and reached near extinction in the early 1950s. The preference of suckers and whitefish for shallower areas initially spared them from the full impact of sea lamprey predation, but eventually numbers were also reduced greatly by the gradual and persistent inroads of this predator. However, reduction in catch of suckers and whitefish in recent years can also be attributed to declining fishing effort. The program of sea lamprey control, made possible by discovery of a selective lamprey poison in the late 1950s, and lake trout rehabilitation now in progress should improve the stocks of these three species. Steelhead trout were introduced to Lake Michigan prior to lamprey control, and these populations are also expected to rebound, as they have since 1965.

Catches of lake herring, traditionally the most productive species of Lake Michigan, declined sharply after 1954. Although the cause of this decline is uncertain, it has coincided with the establishment and increase of the alewife. Since the alewife first became abundant in the areas inhabited by the lake herring, there is a strong possibility of incompatibility between the two species and a competitive advantage favoring the alewife. If this is true, it is considered unlikely that lake herring stocks will improve. The walleye became important in Lake Michigan in the late 1940s. This increase resulted from one extremely strong year class that hatched in 1943 in Green Bay. The catch continued high through the 1950s, with the support of other less successful hatches. The catch has declined recently. The influence of sea lamprey predation on the Green Bay stocks seems to have been minor. Hence, the fluctuations in the stocks there must have resulted from variable success in hatching and survival in certain years owing to unknown environmental or physiological factors. The walleyes that live along the shore of the open lake have contributed relatively little to the catches. The future of the walleye stocks in Lake Michigan is unpredictable, and depends largely on the unknown factors that influence the suitability of the environment during incubation, hatching, and early life.

Yellow perch have always been abundant in the shore and bay areas of Lake Michigan, and consistently have made a substantial contribution to the commercial and sport catch. The catch has increased substantially since the early 1950s. The higher production reflects an increase in abundance which has more than doubled in most areas of the Lake since 1950. The larger numbers may have resulted from a number of influences which include: increased availability of smelt as food in the early 1950s, greater numbers of small chubs as food in the mid-1950s, large quantities of alewives as food in the early 1960s, enrichment of inshore areas as a result of greater bottom mixing during recent low lake levels, and possible enrichment of littoral currents and bays by tributaries carrying a progressively greater load of organic materials. Whatever the causes, the abundance of yellow perch at present is at the highest level of record in Lake Michigan. The duration of this increase is uncertain, however, since the species composition in shallow areas is changing rapidly in response to increased dredging, pollution, and so on.

The chubs, although abundant throughout the history of the commercial fishery, have undergone extreme changes in population structure. Until the 1950s, the chub population of Lake Michigan consisted of seven species that had different growth rates and occupied different depth zones of the lake. Some chubs grew faster than others. One species, the bloater (*Coregonus hoyi*) grew very slowly and seldom attained large size. The two largest species, which along with the lake trout and burbot were preyed upon heavily by the sea lamprey, were very scarce in the early 1950s, and apparently were extinct by 1960. As the lake trout, burbot, and largest chubs vanished, the sea lamprey depended on the four species of chubs of intermediate size and growth. These were the only deep water fish remaining of suitable size for sea lampreys to feed upon. These four chubs also were heavily fished by the commercial fishery during and following the period of lake trout decline. Their numbers decreased rapidly during the 1950s, and by 1963 they constituted less than one percent of the chub stocks taken in nonselective trawls. The bloaters, which once were the main food of lake trout, had no major predator following trout declines; they were too small for the sea lamprey to feed on and were not large enough to meet the requirements of the human food markets. Thus, the bloater was favored in the pressures that influenced the chub stocks, and it became extremely abundant during the 1950s. It now constitutes over 99 percent of the chub population. The number of bloaters in southern and central Lake Michigan in 1960 was about equal to the total number of chubs of all species before the sea lamprey invasion. In northern Lake Michigan, however, where chubs previously were never very abundant, bloaters were about 2.5 times more numerous in 1961 than all species combined before the sea lamprey invasion.

Before 1950, the bloater was found mostly at intermediate depths (20 to 45 fathoms), but now it is abundant throughout the entire deep-water area of the lake. Although it has increased many times in number, the total number of all chubs in Lake Michigan has not changed greatly, except in the northern end of the Lake, as mentioned above. As the bloater spread throughout the entire Lake it underwent two obvious biological changes. The appearance of individual fish became much more variable, possibly owing to hybridization with other species of chubs that had become very scarce, and to the occupation of a greater range of habitat. Also, its growth has changed, and the average length of bloaters taken in nonselective trawl samples was as much as 1.5 inches longer in 1960 than in 1954. Thus, bloaters are no longer the small chubs of the past. They are used extensively in the human food market. Smaller bloaters are now taken in trawls for animal food, and larger bloaters are probably the primary sustenance for the sea lampreys of Lake Michigan.

Of species that were introduced or have invaded Lake Michigan, only the carp, smelt, and alewife have become abundant enough to make substantial contributions to the commercial catch within the lake. The carp, which was introduced into the Lake in the late 1800s, is now found in all shallow areas of Lake Michigan. It is most abundant in Green Bay, and in the extensive shallow areas of the northeast and southern sections of the Lake. It was first recorded in commercial catch statistics in 1893 when about 2,000 pounds were taken. The catch increased steadily, and since 1934 has varied between 1 and 2 million pounds annually. The market demand for carp is not great and the catch does not reflect its abundance, particularly since a substantial portion of the yield is taken in gear fished for other species. Continued enrichment of bays and inshore areas, particularly in the southern basin of Lake Michigan by runoff from agricultural areas and by domestic and industrial wastes, has enhanced conditions favorable to carp. Present trends indicate that this enrichment will increase, so it is likely that present stocks of carp will continue or increase.

Smelt were introduced into Torch and Crystal Lakes, which are tributary to Lake Michigan, in 1912. They escaped from these waters into Lake Michigan (where they were first taken in 1923), spread rapidly throughout the Lake, and became especially abundant in Green Bay. The first commercial catch was recorded in 1931 when 86,000 pounds was taken. Previously, great quantities of smelt were taken by sport fishermen from streams into which these fish migrated to spawn each spring. The catch increased rapidly to about 4.8 million pounds in 1941, but after an extensive die-off in the period 1942 to 1943, it declined to an all-time low of 5,000 pounds in 1944. The smelt subsequently became even more abundant than in 1941. The catch exceeded 9 million pounds in 1958, but has since declined sharply to 1.2 million pounds in 1963. The most recent decline in smelt stocks is coincident with the extreme increase in abundance of alewives, which suggests an incompatible competitive relationship. The present abundance of yellow perch also may influence the smelt as both species occupy the same area of the Lake during much of the year. The future trends in smelt stocks are uncertain because the effect of recent increases in alewives and yellow perch on their abundance is unknown.

The alewife invaded the Great Lakes via the St. Lawrence River and was first recorded in Lake Michigan in 1949. During the early 1950s, it lived mostly in bays, tributaries, and inshore areas, and was seldom taken in the open lake. Extensive sampling with gill nets and trawls throughout the lake in the period 1954 to 1955 failed to take alewives in offshore waters. In 1956, however, the commercial fishery took nearly 500 pounds along the Wisconsin shore, after which the catch increased to over 5 million pounds in 1963. By August, the 1964 catch had surpassed 7 million pounds, and population studies showed that recruitment was still increasing. Despite the sharp increase in production, the catch of alewives has never reached its potential.

Since first being recorded in 1949, the alewife has become the most abundant and widely distributed species in Lake Michigan and is still increasing. It occurs in great abundance throughout the Lake, its bays, and its tributaries at various times of the year. Adult alewives are concentrated in the deeper areas of the Lake in the middle of the winter. In late winter they start a slow movement toward shore. During the spring and early summer they are concentrated in the shore areas, bays, and tributary rivers where they spawn. In late summer and fall, both adults and young of the year slowly move back to the deeper areas of the Lake. Yearling alewives apparently are pelagic, as they are seldom taken on the bottom. Adult alewives, although most common on the bottom, also sometimes inhabit the middepths.

The possible incompatibility of alewives with more desirable species is a subject of increasing concern. Since the alewife occupies all sections of the Lake in great numbers, it undoubtedly influences all species in the Lake. The decline of the lake herring and smelt accompanied the increase of the alewife in both Lakes Michigan and Huron. A third species, the emerald shiner, for which abundance records are not available, also became extremely scarce as the alewife increased. The chubs and whitefish, which compete with alewives for food and space, may also be adversely influenced as the alewife population continues to increase. Even the yellow perch may compete with the alewife for space, although as a predator it may have been favored by the increased food provided by the alewife. Sport fishermen report that fewer yellow perch have been taken in recent years along the shores and near harbor breakwaters—areas where alewives are abundant during the summer sport fishing period.

The extreme abundance of alewife in Lake Michigan culminating in explosive die-offs that were damaging to aesthetics, water recreation, and water quality, were viewed in some fishery circles as an opportunity—that of converting an efficient but low-value forage fish into some valuable, large predator fish. Lake trout rehabilitation by the Bureau of Commercial Fsheries was seen as only a partial answer since that species inhabits largely deep waters. After thorough study, the Pacific salmon, coho (*Oncorhynchus nerka*), and chinook (*O. tshawytscha*) were selected, and in the spring of 1966, 850,000 coho smolts from Oregon were released in three Michigan streams.

In three months, coho weighing up to seven pounds began to appear in commercial gill nets. By September, immature males (jacks) were ascending the planting streams and creating excitement among sport fishermen previously unheard of on the Great Lakes. Growth rates exhibited by these and subsequent plantings of coho and chinook have exceeded those for the native Pacific Ocean. Adults returning to planting streams have supplied abundant eggs for continuation of this remarkable fishery success story, and fish in excess of hatchery needs have opened a new form of commercial fishery.

Several factors have risen to cloud the success of salmon in the Lakes, however, especially in Lake Michigan. Incubation success of coho eggs in hatcheries has been disappointingly poor. Experiments have indicated that hatching failure may be due to toxicity of pesticides incorporated in the fatty yolk. In the spring of 1969, commercially processed salmon derived from the spawning run, was impounded by the U.S. Food and Drug Administration because of levels of pesticides, principally DDT and dieldrin, which made it unsafe for human consumption. There are also speculations about the feasibility of establishing a stable population balance between the alewife (prey) and salmon (predator). While the pesticide question is creating urgent reevaluations of water and land use in the Basin, the question of population stability may be of more lasting importance for a sustained sport and commercial fishery.

The structure of Lake Michigan fish populations has been undergoing radical changes in recent years, as the above discussion indicates. With the continued increase in alewife abundance, the control of the sea lamprey, the reintroduction of the lake trout, the introduction of coho and chinook salmon, and planned introductions of Atlantic salmon and steelhead trout, all taking place relatively simultaneously, the fish stocks of Lake Michigan will undoubtedly remain in a state of extreme instability for an indefinite period. The complex interrelations among the species, and the relation of the individual species with the environment, which is also changing rapidly, can be understood only through intensive studies of the fish stocks and environmental influences. Present studies on the Lake fall far short of these needs, and can do no more than lead to the limited evaluations and speculations.

Traditionally, Lake Erie has produced the greatest variety of commercially important fishes of any of the Great Lakes. No less than 17 species have been significant in the landings at one time or another in the more than 150 years since fishing began. Of these, three species, the smelt, carp, and goldfish, were deliberate or inadvertent introductions to the Lake. Annual production in the past 50 years has averaged approximately 50 million pounds and has often equaled the combined production of the other four Lakes. In all years where complete or nearly complete records exist, Lake Erie has accounted for at least a third of the total Great Lakes fish production. Presumably, the more advanced trophic state of the lake and its shallowness have been responsible for its greater productivity.

Early catch records suggest fairly stable fish populations until 1913, and reflect the loss of only one major fishery—that for the sturgeon. Populations of lake herring or cisco decreased markedly in 1925 and showed no recovery in subsequent years except for a brief improvement in the period 1945 to 1946 when commercial catches reached levels comparable to those in the early years. Since 1957 this species has become, for all practical purposes, commercially extinct. No definite reason for the disappearance of the cisco fishery has been established, mainly because knowledge of the factors responsible for the levels of abundance during the earlier years of normal production was lacking and because no detailed investigations were made in the years of the collapse. During this same period, the northern pike (*Esox lucius*) also began to disappear from commercial catches following an abrupt decline in abundance in 1915. Present day catches of this species are negligible.

A period of great instability in Lake Erie fish populations began in the early 1950s. Smelt appeared in commercially important numbers about 1953. Production of smelt increased dramatically in Canada throughout the remainder of the decade, while United States landings were reduced as three high value species, the sauger, whitefish, and blue pike declined drastically in abundance.

Between 1913 and 1954, whitefish populations fluctuated somewhat cyclically. Commercially available fish declined abruptly in 1955 and then continued a trend sharply downward in subsequent years that was without historical parallel. In 1963, less than 1000 pounds was landed.

In the period 1913–1957, blue pike (*Stizostedion uitreum glaucum*) production in Lake Erie displayed no long-term departure from average, although annual yields were characterized by drastic fluctuations. Following an unprecedented drop in landings in 1958, the fishery collapsed completely, with only nominal catches made after that year.

Deterioration of the stocks of saugers (*Stizotedion canadense*), with an accompanying decrease in commercial production, antedates that of the whitefish and blue pike. Like the blue pike, populations were characterized by drastic fluctuations, but until about 1945, no long-term departure from average was evident. Between 1946 and 1958, commercial production declined steadily and rapidly. Now commercially extinct, the sauger may also be approaching biological extinction in Lake Erie.

As with the cisco fishery some decades earlier, no definite reason for the disappearance of the whitefish, blue pike, and sauger stocks has been established. Long-term cyclic changes in abundance due to equally long-term changes in climatic conditions, irreversible changes in the environment aided by pollution that affected a particular life history stage, and excessive exploitation are some suggested causes. It is possible that two or more of these factors may be simultaneously responsible.

With traditional fish populations in Lake Erie essentially extinct, attention has been shifted principally toward walleye, yellow perch, and smelt. Ample populations of these fish are available that are underfished in most years, although there have been some major fluctuations in abundance. Walleye appear to be on a downward trend since 1956 in the western basin (perhaps due to pollution), but stocks in the eastern basin show no similar decline. Yellow perch are fished extensively for sport through the ice in winter. Many of these are sold commercially. Smelt were apparently derived from Lake Michigan, being first reported in Lake Erie in 1931. The principal fishery is in Canadian waters during the spring spawning runs.

Normally, the smelt frequents the deeper water of the central and eastern basins. Migrations into the western basin occur only during the winter and early spring months. Studies by Canadian biologists have demonstrated a variable but generally good hatch and survival of the species in all recent years. Consequently, in spite of substantial annual harvests, a sizable population of fish is still available to the fishery.

Lake Erie supports large populations of sheepshead (*Archosargus probatocephalus*), a potentially useful commercial fish. Its principal significance today is as a competitor with other species for both space and food. White bass (*Roccus chrysops*) and channel catfish (*Ictalurers punctatus*) are also important lake fishes.

Alewife and gizzard shad are the principal noxious fish in Lake Erie. The alewife invaded the Great Lakes via the St. Lawrence River and was first recorded in Lake Erie in 1931. Subsequently, it became established at a modest level of density, never attaining the pestiferous proportions that characterized its invasion of Lakes Huron and Michigan. The gizzard shad is indigenous to Lake Erie and has exhibited drastic population fluctuations in the past. In 1958, water intakes of power plants and other installations in western Lake Erie were clogged by the huge numbers of gizzard shad locally present. During the same period, sudden shifts in thermal gradients in Erie Harbor, Pennsylvania, caused massive gizzard shad die-offs, estimated to be at least a million pounds, creating serious removal problems. Fluctuating though these explosions of presently noncommercial species are, they represent a huge biomass currently tied up in nonproductive uses.

Less is known of the past history and population dynamics of Lake Ontario fish than those of any of the other Great Lakes.

Although the commercial fish production of Lake Ontario throughout the period of record has been relatively low in comparison with other lakes, particularly its fertile neighbor, Lake Erie, the annual catches have contributed significantly to Great Lakes production.

At the time of earliest settlement, Atlantic salmon were plentiful and spawned in most of the streams along the north shore as well as the Salmon and Oswego Rivers on the southern shore. The Salmon River, according to early reports, supported the best runs in United States waters of Lake Ontario, with as many as 300 salmon being taken by one fisherman in a single night's fishing. Under this pressure, plus construction of dams on the spawning tributaries, the fishery declined until, somewhere between 1880 and 1900, Lake Ontario salmon became entirely extinct. Study of the scales from museum specimens indicates that these salmon were a land-locked form that did not ascend the St. Lawrence River from the sea.

Whitefish and lake trout were also commercially taken in Lake Ontario from the earliest times. A considerable number of sturgeon and lake herring were caught, but were considered to have no value at the time and were destroyed. Later the lake herring became quite important in the commercial fishery, but the sturgeon had virtually disappeared by the time its commercial potential began to be appreciated. As the fishery developed, blue pike, chubs, walleye, yellow perch, and eels began to be harvested in increasing numbers. Late in the nineteenth century the carp was introduced, followed by the smelt in the 1940s and the white perch in the 1950s. They have since become a significant part of the total fish stocks of the Lake, with the carp and smelt entering into the commercial fishery. It is not definitely known whether the alewife was indigenous to Lake Ontario or came in as an invader, as was the case in the other Great Lakes. In any event, the species has been abundant in Lake Ontario since at least 1890, and has experienced annual die-offs of nuisance proportions in recent years, especially along the south shore.

During the first three decades of the twentieth century, the basic resource apparently reached some sort of equilibrium with man's influence and limited biological changes such as the appearance of the carp, and possibly the alewife. The commercial fishery maintained itself in a fairly flourishing condition. Although the salmon and sturgeon had passed from the scene, the cold water complex still retained the lake trout, whitefish, lake herring, and chubs as important contributors during this period. The higher value warm water species such as the blue pike and yellow perch remained at a high production level, with some input from walleye and the introduced carp.

In recent years, cold water commercial fish production has declined considerably. The lake trout fishery has virtually disappeared. Commercial whitefish production is now restricted to the eastern end of the Lake.

The blue pike has been lost commercially, if not biologically, to the Lake Ontario fishery complex. What is left of the United States warm water commercial fishery is largely dependent on the carp and yellow perch. A popular recreational fishery exists in the island areas of the eastern basin, the St. Lawrence River, and the Bay of Quinte, and near populated bays on the south shore. Species involved in this fishery are: small-mouth bass, yellow perch, northern pike, muskellunge, and walleye.

Lake Ontario supports large populations of species such as alewives and smelt which are essentially unused commercially. Smelt are heavily utilized in spawning run sport fisheries, however.

The reasons for the limited productivity of the Lake Ontario commercial fishery in contrast to the other Great Lakes are not fully understood. Some influences such as introduction of new species and poor markets for abundant but low-value species have also worked against the commercial fishery of other lakes. It seems apparent that excessive harvest of lake trout over very restricted spawning areas has had severely adverse effects and may largely account for declines in this species. Limnological changes due to man's influence have also had an influence. However, other Great Lakes have had similar changes which in some cases, such as Lake Erie, have had greater impact. Morphological considerations are sometimes cited to account for Lake Ontario's low productivity. While great depths do prevail over much of the Lake, Lake Ontario has roughly the same percentage of shallow, shoal water as Lake Michigan, and a greater percentage than Lake Superior, thus casting considerable doubt on this explanation.

The sea lamprey, whose recent invasion of the Upper Great Lakes has been a major catastrophe to their fisheries, has always been present in Lake Ontario. Some sort of biological equilibrium between the lamprey and other species was achieved long ago, although lamprey predations still continue to exert at least a peripheral influence upon fish population dynamics. The equilibrium is not a stable one, however.

As in other Great Lakes, large predator fish, principally chinook and coho salmon, have been introduced via tributaries deemed suitable for spawning runs. The success of these fish has not been demonstrated in Lake Ontario, although there is little reason to suspect failure in view of successes in Lake Michigan. Most attempts to analyze and explain past and even current dynamics of the fish populations in Lake Ontario are largely speculative. If future management is to be more effective and meaningful, a much sounder basis of study and investigation must be established.

It is certain that environmental changes in the Lakes and their tributaries and species introductions via engineering works are causing widespread and quite rapid changes in the ecology of the Great Lakes. These changes are reflected in commercial fish catches, in the sport fishery, and in the quality of waters used by industry, by municipalities, and for water-based recreation. Most of these changes have been toward the negative side. Some, for example salmon introductions, have had pronounced benefits. It is ironic that untoward effects of pesticides on salmon restrict the utility of even this spectacular biological success, however. Most ecological changes cannot be remedied by minor policy decisions or small-scale tributary cleanups. They require the attention of no less than broad-scale, regional planning, research and implementation.

References

Ayers, J. D., D. V. Anderson, D. C. Chandler, and G. H. Lauff. 1956. Currents and water masses of Lake Huron. Univ. Mich., Great Lakes Res. Div., Publ. No. 1, 101 pp.

Beeton, Alfred M. 1958. Relationship between Secchi disk readings and light penetration in Lake Huron. Trans. Am. Fish. Soc., 87(1957): 73–79.

Beeton, Alfred M. 1969. The vertical migration of *Mysis relicta* in Lakes Huron and Michigan. Jour. Fish. Res. Bd. Canada, 17(4): 517–539.

Beeton, Alfred M. and D. C. Chandler. 1963. The St. Lawrence Great Lakes. In: Limnology in North America, Univ. Wis. Press, Madison, Chap. 19: 535–558.

Beeton, A. M., J. H. Johnson, and S. H. Smith. 1959. Lake Superior limnological data. U.S. Fish and Wildl. Serv., Spec. Sci. Rept., Fish. No. 297, 177 p.

Beeton, Alfred M., Stanford H. Smith, and Frank H. Hooper. 1967. Physical limnology of Saginaw Bay, Lake Huron. Great Lakes Fish. Comm., Tech. Rept. No. 12, 56 pp.

Brinkhurst, Ralph O. 1967. The distribution of aquatic oligochaetes in Saginaw Bay, Lake Huron. Limnol. and Oceanog., 12(1): 137–143.

Britt, N. Wilson, 1955. Stratification in western Lake Erie in summer of 1953; effects on the *Hexagenia* (Ephemeroptera) population. Ecol., 36: 239–244.

Bureau of Commercial Fisheries. 1965. R/V *Kaho* Cruise Report No. 27, Exploratory Fishing Survey of Lake Huron. FWS, Bureau of Commercial Fisheries, Branch of Exploratory Fishing, Ann Arbor, Michigan. 7 pp.

―――. 1965. Report on Commercial Fisheries Resources of the Lake Michigan Basin. (Processed.)

―――. 1966. R/V *Kaho* Cruise Report No. 35 (Lake Huron). FWS, Bureau of Commercial Fisheries, Branch of Exploratory Fishing, Ann Arbor, Michigan. 8 pp.

―――. 1966. Report on Commercial Fisheries Resources of the Lake Erie Basin. (Processed.)

―――. 1968. Report on Commercial Fisheries Resources of the Lake Huron Basin. (Processed.)

―――. 1969. Report on Commercial Fisheries Resources of the Lake Ontario Basin. (Processed.)

Cooper, John E. 1962. Seasonal changes with depth in population of *Pontoporeia affinis* (Amphipoda) in South Bay, Lake Huron. Univ. Mich., Great Lakes Res. Div., Publ. 9: 173 (Abst.; Proc. 5th Conf.).

Davis, Charles C. 1964. Evidence for the eutrophication of Lake Erie from phytoplankton records. Limnol. Oceanog., 9: 275–283.

―――. 1966. Plankton studies in the largest Great Lakes of the world with special reference to the St. Lawrence Great Lakes of North America. Univ. Mich., Great Lakes Res. Div., Publ. 14: 1–36.

Fry, F. E. J. 1956. Movements of drift cards in Georgian Bay in 1953. Jour. Fish. Res. Bd. Canada, 13(1): 1–5.

Great Lakes Institute, University of Toronto. 1964. Great Lakes Institute annual report, 1963. Univ. Toronto, Great Lakes Inst., Prelim. Rept. No. 15, 91 pp.

Hachey, H. B. 1952. Vertical temperature distribution in the Great Lakes. Jour. Fish. Res. Bd. Canada, 9(7): 325–328.

Hile, Ralph and Howard J. Buettner. 1959. Fluctuations in the commercial fisheries of Saginaw Bay 1885–1956. FWS, Res. Rept. No. 51: 1–38.

Johnson, J. H. 1958. Surface-current studies of Saginaw Bay and Lake Huron, 1956. FWS, Spec. Sci. Rept., Fish. No. 267. 84 pp.

Leverin, H. A. 1947. Industrial waters of Canada. Report on investigations, 1934 to 1943. Canadian Dept. Mines Research, Mines Geol. Branch, Rept. No. 819, 109 pp.

Millar, F. G. 1952. Surface temperatures in the Great Lakes. Jour. Fish Res. Bd. Canada, 9(7): 329–376.

Miller, Robert R. 1957. Origin and dispersal of the alewife, *Alosa pseudoharangus,* and the gizzard shad, *Doropoma Copedianum,* in the Great Lakes. Trans. Am. Fish. Soc., 86(1956): 97–111.

Neil, John H. and Glenn E. Owen. 1964. Distribution, Environmental requirements and significance of *Cladophora* in the Great Lakes. Univ. Mich., Great Lakes Res. Div., Publ. 11: 113–121 (Proc. 7th Conf.).

New York State Department of Health. 1958. Lake Ontario surface water including specified tributaries. Lake Ontario Drainage Basin Surv. Ser., Rept. No. 4. 447 pp.

Putnam, H. D., and T. A. Olson. 1961. Studies on the productivity and plankton of Lake Superior. School Pub. Health, Univ. Minnesota, 72 pp. (Mimeo).

Robertson, Andrew. 1966. The distribution of calanoid copepods in the Great Lakes. Univ. Mich., Great Lakes Res. Div., Publ. 15: 129–139 (Proc. 9th Conf.).

Rodgers, G. K. 1965. The thermal bar in the Laurentian Great Lakes. Univ. Mich., Great Lakes Res. Div., Publ. 13: 358–363 (Proc. 8th Conf.).

Ruschmeyer, O. R., T. A. Olson, and H. M. Bosch. 1958. Water movements and temperatures of western Lake Superior. School Pub. Health, Univ. Minnesota, 65 pp. (Mimeo).

Schuytema, Gerald S. and Ross E. Powers. 1966. The distribution of benthic fauna in Lake Huron. Univ. Mich., Great Lakes Res. Div., Publ. 15: 155–163 (Proc. 8th Conf.).

Teter, H. E. 1960. The bottom fauna of Lake Huron. Trans. Amer. Fish. Soc., 89(1959): 193–197.

C

Biological and Chemical Submodels

G. E. Raines, D. D. Koob *

The biological response models stress the analysis of the biological communities in the environmental subsystem under examination. This will include analysis pertaining to algae, bacteria and fungi, zooplankton, protozoa, benthos, and fish. A comprehensive, rather than a limited approach, is at this point necessary since no one biological category can be adequately described or studied without directly affecting the other biological components of the ecosystem. Individually the algae are important as primary producers and as unsightly habitat contaminators; the fish are of economic importance for commercial harvest and for sport fishery; the bacterial and fungal populations aid in nutrient recycling and are undoubtedly the prime cause of oxygen depletion. However, the growth of the algal population is dependent upon the rates of nutrient supply from bacterial metabolism, the rates of removal by graying organisms, the extent of parasitism by microorganism, and upon numerous physical and chemical factors. The standing crops and change in biomass with time of each of the biological population are due to a complex interaction among all of these categories. This complex chain is shown in Figure C-1.

As noted previously, the research approach is to establish a hierarchical system of models. The upper echelon model, a highest echelon model, correlates information from all of the lower echelon systems one generation removed. This regression continues until the information from the lowest echelon model or models is obtained. Echelon models on the same hierarchical level would of necessity have to be linked together when dependence is implied. This aspect will become very evident as the strong dependence of the biological system on the Lakes' chemical structure is revealed in the following discussion and figures. Therefore, the two submodels discussed separately within this appendix would be linked in an appropriate manner.

The procedure proven most fruitful for initially investigating such a system is to first design a generalized block diagram showing the trophic interrelationships for all of the important biological components. This has been represented as an internal or central ring in Figure C-1. Next, each major component is enlarged to show the relationships of the various physical, chemical, and biological factors to the population(s) in question. Block diagrams for five major populations shown in Figure C-1 are provided in Figures C-2 through C-6. A composite of the entire biological response system can thereby be developed by linking Figures C-1 through C-6 together.

---

* Mr. Koob is now at Utah State University, Logan, Utah.

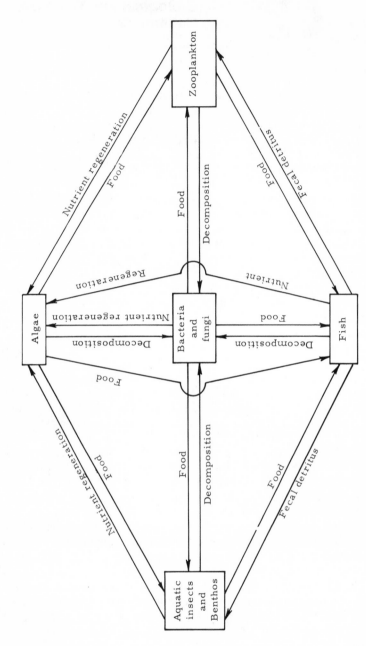

Figure C-1. Gross Trophic Relationships among the Plant and Animal Populations of the Lake Erie Aquatic Ecosystem

Biological Submodel

The modeling of each major biological compartment would be based upon the expression of biomass as a continuous dependent variable, depending explicitly on the ordinary differential equations based on pertinent physical, chemical, and biological variables. In this way, biologically significant, as well as economically important, changes in any of the populations can be anticipated. This would include the development of algal masses, depletion of plankton food organisms, and changes in the size of the fishery.

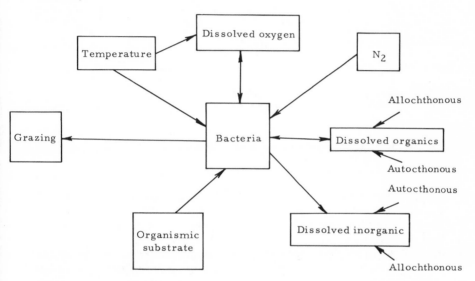

Figure C-2. Effects of Various Factors on the Bacterial Population

As an example in point, the ordinary differential equation for the dynamics of a specific category of a fish population is based on the fact that the rate of change of population is equal to the difference between the rate at which fish enter the category (either by reaching the lower age limit of the category or by entering the area considered from another part of the lake or by introduction from a hatchery) and the rate at which fish leave the category (by natural death, natural predation, commercial exploitation, parasitism, death due to introduced toxins, or by reaching the upper age limit, if any, of the category). It is straightforward to write this ordinary differential equation as a sum of + and − terms. Each term can then be expressed to represent the mechanism causing it. Such equations are well known in the literature, although some of the terms need improvement.

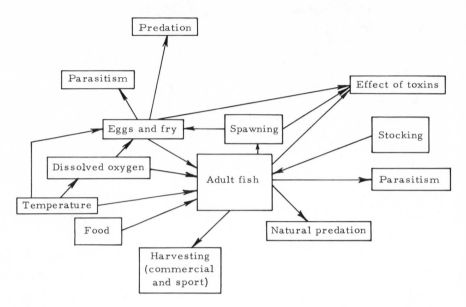

Figure C-3. Interrelationships of Fish Populations with Various Physical, Chemical, and Biological Factors

An interesting special case in the fish population model involves the category of production and survival of eggs. If the age duration of a category is short enough compared with the numerical integration time increment, one can obtain a formula for the rate of exit from the category by a product of several factors: the rate at which entries are made (unfertilized eggs laid per month), the probability of fertilization of an egg, the probability of survival of egghood, the probability of successful hatching, and the probability of survival to the upper age limit of the category. Each of these factors can be represented mathematically in terms of variables in the hierarchy of models, including terms for dissolved oxygen, concentrations of toxic substances, turbidity, water temperature, and so on.

In order to minimize the number of equations and the amount of input data required, it would be expedient to initially employ very gross taxa in defining categories for all organisms during the earlier phases of the effort. Progressive refinement would then be feasible.

In the case of the algal populations, the generalized growth ordinary differential equation would be patterned after the Davidson and Clymer model[1] for phytoplankton (1966), making appropriate minor modifications to include the characteristics of attached algae as well as phytoplankton. Other refinements are also possible. Some of these might be:

(1) The consideration of the importance of the interaction of two or more nutrients. For instance; what is the combined importance of

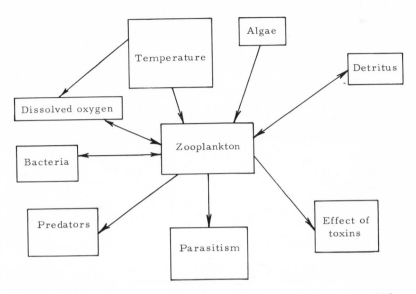

Figure C-4. Some Interrelationships of the Zooplankton Population with Physical, Chemical, and Biological Factors

both nitrate and phosphate? Both have relevance to the term for photosynthesis. The form of the term may be a product, a sum, or a sum and a product.

(2) The necessity to violate the assumption that all species are alike and to deal with two or more taxa, each having its own growth ordinary differential equation which is dependent upon the nutrient concentration ordinary differential equations from Model II.

(3) The necessity of differentiation between rates of growth and rates of reproduction.

(4) The importance of including all organisms which graze on algae rather than limiting this activity to the zooplankton populations. This would modify the zooplankton analogue to algae.

(5) The incorporation of the importance of dissolved oxygen to the rates of growth of the algal populations. This would include specific tolerance values for individual populations.

(6) The importance of parasitism (bacterial, fungal, viral) to the potential growth rates and the resultant biomass production for various algal populations.

(7) The effect of the production of soluble organics (growth substances, vitamins) by the bacterial and fungal populations.

One of the most important ordinary differential equations in the biological response model is the decomposition by bacteria of the algae which have sunk to the bottom and which grow on the bottom. The key to this

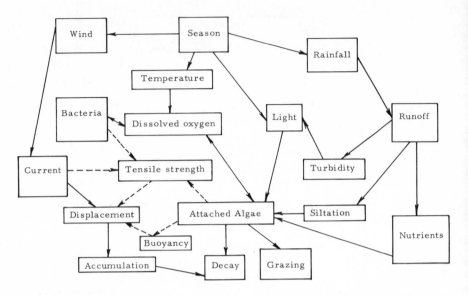

Figure C-5. Effects of Various Factors on the Growth of Attached Algae and the Changes in Properties of these Algae as a Function of these Factors

effect may be an ordinary differential equation for population dynamics for some gross bacterial taxon as affected by available algal biomass, water temperature, dissolved-oxygen concentration, and so on. This ordinary differential equation will include a death term dependent upon accumulation of toxic substances, grazing by bottom organisms, and ingestion by zooplankton. The output from a zooplankton population ordinary differential equation will drive the death term in the bacterial ordinary differential equation. The zooplankton ordinary differential equation, in turn, must contain a death term due to predation by insect and fish populations. One or two insect population ordinary differential equations will provide inputs to the fish ordinary differential equation. A sunken algal biomass ordinary differential equation will drive the bacterial ordinary differential equation. All such ordinary differential equations are straightforward in their derivation. It is reasonable to approximate applicable values for coefficients by considering equilibrium populations which are determined by the algebraic equations obtained by setting the rates of change on the left sides of the ordinary differential equations to zero.

The types of data that would be necessary or desirable for biological submodel include:

    (1) Fish population (ordinary differential equation)
        (a) Rates of stocking from hatcheries
        (b) Rates of recruitment from Category (2) below
        (c) Mortality rates

131

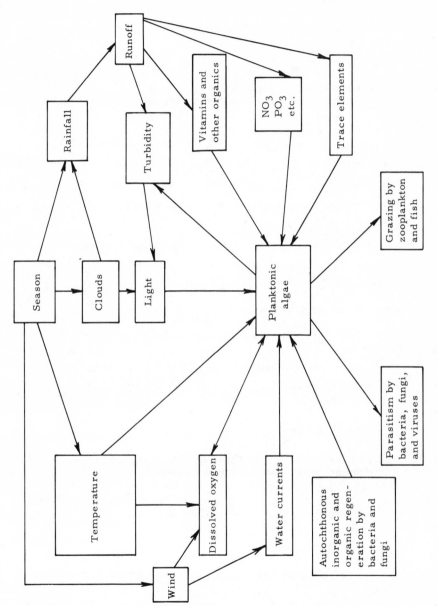

Figure C-6. Generalized Scheme of Chemical, Physical, and Biological Factors Affecting the Phyto-plankton Populations

    (d) Rates of food intake
    (e) Fishing effort in relation to fish populations
    (f) Toxicity to fish of known pollutants
    (g) Rates of predation of fish.
  (2) Fish egg and fry (ordinary differential equation)
    (a) Numbers of eggs spawned
    (b) Efficiency of fertilization
    (c) Toxicity of various pollutants, including low dissolved oxygen
    (d) Rates of predation of eggs and young
    (e) Influence of temperature on spawning.
  (3) Phytoplankton population (ordinary differential equation)
    (a) Growth and reproduction as a function of nutrients, light and temperature
    (b) Toxicity of various pollutants, including low dissolved oxygen
    (c) Grazing-rate coefficient for zooplankton and fish
    (d) Rates of respiration as function of temperature
    (e) Extent of parasitism.
  (4) Attached algae population (ordinary differential equation)
    (a) Growth rate as function of light, temperature, and nutrient concentration
    (b) Algal-filament rupture strength versus current as a function of filament length
    (c) Rates of grazing by fish and benthic organisms
    (d) Rates of siltation and changes in turbidity
    (e) Effects of parasitism as related to Items (a) and (b) above
    (f) Toxicity of various pollutants, including low dissolved oxygen.
  (5) Bacterial population (ordinary differential equation)
    (a) Growth rate as function of availability of substrate, water temperature, and dissolved oxygen
    (b) Grazing by zooplankton
    (c) Effects of various pollutants
    (d) Availability of dissolved organics and inorganics from autochthonous and allochthonous sources.
  (6) Zooplankton population (ordinary differential equation)
    (a) Rate of growth and reproduction as function of food supply and water temperature
    (b) Rate of predation
    (c) Effects of pollutants.

The information needed to construct realistic ordinary differential equations for any of the above categories must come from a wide variety of sources. Some is available in the published literature. Dr. Loren S. Putnam of The Ohio State University is now compiling a bibliography of papers based on work conducted using the facilities of the Franz Theodore Stone Hydrobiological Laboratory. Other relevant papers are scattered through the biological literature journals. Much information resides in the offices of federal, state, and local laboratories. Other data, including individual research papers not pertaining directly to the Great Lakes but definitely applicable to the development of mathematical models, also will be found useful.

Chemical Quality Submodel

A model to predict the chemcial quality of a lake or lake system is essentially a part of the whole environmental system and must receive input from the environment and create output to the environment. Input to the chemistry subsystem must come from impacts such as the atmosphere, inflow to the lake system, bottom sediments, and municipal and industrial wastes added directly to the system or to the inflowing water. Output would affect parts of the environment such as the atmosphere, outflow, and bottom sediments. The relation of the chemistry subsystem to the environment can be depicted as in the block diagram in Figure C-7.

This chemistry subsystem cannot be detailed more thoroughly without loss of generality. Each element or compound must have its own particular chemistry subsystem diagrammed separately in order to include all pertinent details. Then the linkages between each unique chemistry subsystem must be developed to represent the system en toto.

A diagram of an example of one elemental subsystem is presented in Figure C-8 for nitrogen. Now the nitrogen subsystem must be incorporated in the environment as a particular chemistry subsystem which is linked to the environment and to other chemistry subsystems.

A model to predict chemical quality can also be represented as a mass transport model which includes chemical kinetic terms. Mathematical expressions for describing this mass transport are available in the form of a system of partial differential equations which have (1) time and distance as the independent variables; (2) concentration of each material in the water as the dependent variable; and (3) current velocities, turbulent diffusivities, and various rate constants as parameters. Rates and locations of material additions to the lake, as well as shore, surface, and bottom features, form the boundary conditions, while the initial concentrations in the lake form the initial conditions to the system of partial differential equations.

Transient, convective, and dispersion terms in the general form of these partial differential equations are derived from mass transport concepts.[2] Another term represents the effect of biological activity on the concentration of a selected chemical constituent. The biological activity term is actually the next effect of the mathematical models which predict the biological transport of each chemical. If necessary, the biological and chemical quality submodels could be coupled at this point to provide input and feedback from one to another. However, for the purpose of predicting

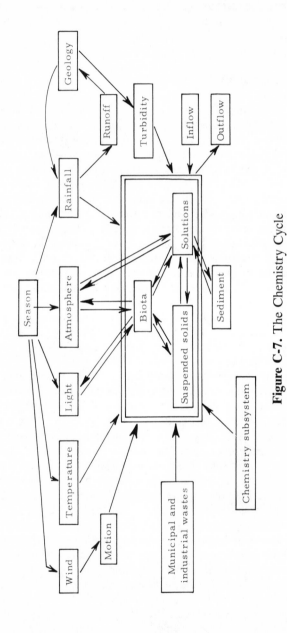

Figure C-7. The Chemistry Cycle

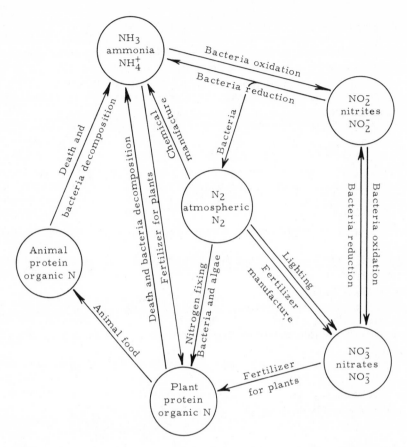

Figure C-8. The Nitrogen Cycle. Source: Clair Sawyer, *Chemistry for Sanitary Engineers* (New York: McGraw Hill, 1960, p. 290).

chemical quality, the net effect of the biological transport models can be given as a known function determined from the biological models or as a gross, simplified version of the biological models. The next term in the generalized equation represents all possible first-order chemical reactions that could generate or destroy a chemical constituent, while another term represents all possible second-order reactions, as determined from concepts of chemical reaction kinetics.[3] A second partial differential equation in the chemical quality model is for heat transfer, and is similar to that for mass transfer.[4]

Mathematical methods are available for solving the general system of differential equations. However, it is seldom necessary to go into such detail for every chemical component in all sections of the lake. A more practical approach is to start with very simple but conservative approximations. A conservative approximation is one which will give high concentrations for those chemicals which are toxic to desirable biological species or important nutrients to undesirable species. Conversely, a conservative approximation will give low concentrations to important nutrients of desirable species. Some chemicals could fall into both categories and their concentration ranges would be bracketed by high and low conservative approximations.

For some chemicals, the simplest approximations might be an adequate description of their distributions and transport. For others, the simplest approximation might be adequate for the entire lake as a whole but certain local areas might require a more detailed description. For these chemicals, only the specific area itself need be modeled in more detail and the results of the simplest model could be used to provide the boundary conditions at the lake boundary of the specific area. For still others, a more detailed model would be required for the entire lake but, even here, the results of the simple model would provide guidance as to the range of concentrations expected and the order of magnitude of various terms in the more detailed equations.

In the simplest model for predicting chemical quality, the entire lake is approximated by a huge, mixed tank. For this approximation, the system of partial differential equations reduces to a system of ordinary differential equations.

Source and sink terms are used to approximate the convective and dispersion terms in the original equation. Some boundary conditions are also included in these source and sink terms. The system of ordinary differential equations consists of N equations, one for each of the N chemical components. A similar equation can also be written to describe the average temperature in the lake, but the temperature equation would be based upon heat transfer theory instead of mass transfer.

The mixed tank model would be applied to all chemicals of concern and temperature. For some chemicals, this model might be an adequate description of their concentration in the water as a function of time and these chemicals would not need to be subjected to more detailed models. For all other chemicals and temperature, the mixed tank model would provide at least a magnitude estimate of the average temperature and chemical concentrations as a function of time within the lake.

A next step in detail would be to segment the lakes into several large sections and apply the mixed tank model to each of the remaining chemicals and the temperature within each section. This model would consist of $(N + 1)S$ simultaneous, ordinary differential equations, where N is the number of chemical components remaining under consideration and S is the number of sections in the lakes. This large-section model would provide the chemical concentrations and temperature within each section as a function of time. Here again, this large-section model might be an adequate description of the concentration of some of the chemicals and also, perhaps, the temperature.

From this large-section model, there are several approaches toward arriving at more detail. The sectioning process can continue with the lake being divided into smaller and smaller sections. This amounts to developing a finite difference approximation to the original equations. Another approach is to reexamine the models in light of the information obtained in the mixed tank and large-section models. With this information, it might be possible to obtain approximate solutions for certain areas of the lake and use these approximate solutions for the detailed description. Still another approach would use the information from the mixed tank and large-section models in order to determine other finite difference approximations. The particular method to be used would depend on this information.

These steps in the development of chemical quality models offer the most practical methods for obtaining adequate descriptions of the chemical concentrations and temperature in the lake and with enough detail to assess the consequences of any discharge into the lake. The types of data required for these models include:

(1) identification of the important chemicals in the lake and their chemical forms (for example, as inorganic ions or organic compounds);

(2) chemical kinetic rates for all significant chemical interactions;

(3) directions and magnitudes of the prevailing currents in the lake;

(4) values of turbulent diffusivities in the lake; and

(5) present concentration of all the important chemicals in the lake.

Initially, these data would be obtained from the literature and any omissions would be filled with judicious estimates. Eventually, if the detail and precision were required, the omissions might be filled by field and laboratory experiments.

D Advances in Computer Technology

R. T. Jaske, M. S. Edwards

During a program of such protracted length as is being suggested, there would surely be many developments in computer technology. Some of these would, in turn, have an important impact on the field of computer modeling and simulation. Therefore, it would be imperative to monitor quite closely advances in computer technology as they are being developed, so as to guarantee maximum utility of the models ultimately developed.

In addition to the unforeseen developments that are bound to occur, certain trends already established can be expected to have a significant effect. Certainly the historic trend to digital computers with higher speeds, larger memories, decreased cost per computation, and improved software is expected to continue at a substantial rate. This will, of course, tend to make the simulation of increasingly complex systems more practical.

The following advances can be expected in computer technology.

Time Sharing. Time sharing systems, including the rapidly expanding technology of remote terminals and computer communications networks, help to reduce the overall cost of computer use by making for more efficient machine utilization.

It is generally believed that commercial services will continue to exploit this technology by offering increasingly more powerful remote computing services on a widespread scale. It is possible that such services will eventually provide the user with the heretofore unknown advantages of ready access to a variety of computers, programming languages, and applications programs—enabling him to pick and choose to suit his immediate needs, rather than being effectively limited to one computer and its particular complement of software, as is now so often the case. At present, more services of this type cater only to relatively small time-shared applications having very limited input/output requirements. However, there is already increasing use of larger remote terminals (or small computers), with a full complement of input/output equipment, to run large as well as small jobs on a remote computer. Of special interest to the proposed program is the possibility of low-cost computer access for local planning agencies who may wish to use lower echelon models to explore means of correcting local or regional problems.

Hybrid Systems. Recent advances have made possible the automatic linkage of digital and analog computer systems into a single package termed a hybrid computer.

By combining the characteristics of analog and digital computers in one system, hybrid computers offer much greater speed and versatility in certain applications—particularly those in which there is a requirement for what are inherently digital calculations as well as systems of differential equations that must be solved at high speed. Although hybrid computers have so far been used primarily in military and space applications, their usefulness in many other areas (even agricultural studies, for example) is beginning to be exploited. Capabilities of such dual systems are constantly increasing, and means for making their interaction more efficient are constantly being developed. It is likely that at least some of the simulation needs of the suggested study could eventually best be served by hybrid equipment.

Input. Strides are also being made that render it possible to eliminate much of the man-effort (data reduction, key punching, and so on) involved in entering input data to a computerized system. For example, automatic environmental monitoring systems are available for collecting continuous data on environmental factors (wind speed, water temperature, and so on) which may be important parameters or independent variables in an overall model. Capabilities are now developing for direct input of these data into computer memory systems. Other developments relate to digitizing equipment for automatically coding graphical input data such as plots, map contours, and so on. Systems for the automatic coding of handwritten data and programs are also over the horizon. Voice input is also a future possibility. In a somewhat different but related vein, it is reasonable to expect that systems will also appear for automatically sorting out bad data and/or detecting malfunctions in automatic monitoring equipment.

Output. Significant capabilities have been developed recently for the graphic display of output data as opposed to the conventional tabulated form. The first developments along these lines were the automatic plotters which have been available for about 5 years.

Graphics and interactive computing should also exert increasing influence on simulation. Hardware has been available for some time in the form of high-speed microfilm recorders that can record large amounts of graphical, numerical, or even textual output directly from the computer for later analysis. The much newer on-line consoles and graphics terminals can display selected results in the form of data, graphs, charts, and pictures, almost instantaneously as these are generated in the computer. These latter devices—through attached keyboards, light pens, drawing tablets, and the like—also provide a means for the user to interact with the computer, and therefore to control the course of the calculation on the basis of the information he sees displayed. These recent developments include use of cathode-ray tubes for outputs in not only two but three dimensions. Further, the capability is being developed to continuously change the perspective on 3-D outputs so that important effects can be observed from any angle. On the horizon is the use of color TV systems to develop three-dimensional colored response surfaces to facilitate simultaneous study of multivariate effects. These capabilities will be invaluable in sensitivity analysis work where one wishes to observe instantaneously the effect of changes in selected input variables on some output response surface.

In addition to calculated results, portions of the program itself could be displayed and the program debugged or otherwise modified while on-line to the computer. As is so often the case in the hardware/software relationship, the principal factor deterring wider use of such devices and techniques is the rather sophisticated software required. This must frequently be tailored not only to the particular device and application, but to the computer, operating system, and programming language to be used. Thus, what is accomplished at one installation may be of little direct use to the computing community at large.

Programming Languages. General purpose programming languages such as FORTRAN are frequently used for systems modeling and simulation. Also, a variety of programming languages have been developed specifically for simulation, although usually not more than one or two of these are available for use with a given computer and operating system. Simulation languages have tended to develop along two separate lines: those for discrete change models (SIMSCRIPT, GPSS, and the newer SIMULA being examples of this type) and those for continuous change models (for example, MIMIC, CSMP, and CSSL). Languages in the latter class tend to make the digital computer appear somewhat like an analog computer, at least in the programmer's eye. Either type of language can be a powerful tool within its range of application. However, what is needed and to be hoped for in the future—rather more than a further proliferation of languages and types of languages—is a period of consolidation, standardization, and removal of deficiencies. One deficiency shared by these languages, at least as they are usually implemented, is frequently so critical as to preclude their use in large-scale simulations, even when the model fits neatly into the discrete or continuous category. That is, the languages do not provide for effective use of the computer's secondary storage, leaving no recourse should the program overflow central memory. Furthermore, when a sizable simulation is being contemplated, there is frequently no way of determining in advance whether this will happen. This is one reason why FORTRAN, which suffers no such drawback, is sometimes used. Simulation languages, however, can and have been modified to enable secondary storage to be used for both program segments and data, and it is hoped this will become the rule rather than the exception in future implementations. Encouragement should be lent in this direction by the fact that random access bulk storage devices are becoming so much faster and more economical to use, and that software generally is being oriented more toward these devices.

Cost. Owing to time sharing and other advances in computer hardware design and manufacturing, leading primarily to increased memory and speed capability, computer costs per unit of work are decreasing. It is probably fair to estimate that costs have decreased by about 50 percent in the last three years.

These as well as other advances in computer technology will no doubt be commonplace in the near future. It is essential to monitor these developments and through a management information system to collect, process, store, evaluate, and disseminate these state-of-the-art advances.

A Method for Estimating Recreation Benefits

F. J. Cesario

Over the past several years Battelle has been conducting research aimed at improving methods and estimating benefits of outdoor recreation. The research has been successful in advancing the state-of-the-art. The methods developed have, furthermore, been tested in an actual application to a system of state parks in the mid-Atlantic region. They would be equally applicable to the problem of estimating benefits related to either the development of new recreation sites along the shores of the Great Lakes or to the reopening of beaches that have recently been closed down.

This appendix presents the conceptual framework of the Battelle benefit estimation model. This presentation involves both identifying the major factors or variables involved in the model and hypothesizing relationships among these relevant variables. To serve as a basis for this presentation, it is first necessary to define the recreation system that the model purports to describe.

The Recreation System

The recreation system of interest has three basic components: (1) a set of population centers from which the recreation participants come; (2) a set of roads and highways over which participants travel from the population centers to their recreation destinations; and (3) a set of well-defined sites at which outdoor-recreation services and activities are provided.

Population Centers

The population unit (for example, state, SMSA, county, township, city, and so on) for study is chosen arbitrarily. Ideally, in order to measure the most relevant distance factors, it would be preferable to choose the population unit such that all people residing in this unit can be considered concentrated at a point. For practical reasons, it would be preferable to choose the population unit such that data are readily available on both the population magnitude and characteristics. Taking both of these as well as the spatial distribution of parks into consideration, the unit chosen for use in most studies is the county. Since a county tends to have its weighted mean population location in or near its major city, the distance measurement error does not normally cause appreciable problems. It is only when there are several main cities in a county that difficulty is encountered.

Data on population characteristics are readily available in the various U.S. Census publications.

Recreation Sites

A recreation site in this study is any limited access area set aside for the undertaking of any combination of the following activities: swimming, picnicking, boating, fishing, hiking, sightseeing, and camping. The recreation sites in question are usually built up around natural or manmade lakes, although the study is not necessarily restricted to water-based recreation sites. Though differences in quality are allowed, the parks are assumed to be homogeneous with respect to external factors such as advertising and climate. Representative of the parks that meet the above criteria are state parks and utility company public access areas. These types of parks are the focal point of the study.

Roads and Highways

The roads and highways connect each population unit with each recreation site. There is usually a plurality of different routes to reach a park from each population center. Some routes are preferred to others by any one visitor. Other things being equal, it is assumed that the traveller will choose the route which takes him the least time to traverse. When other things—for instance, tolls—are not equal, however, it is difficult to specify arbitrarily a route that will likely be taken by the majority of people. However, it is convenient for analysis purposes to consider a single value for travel times or money cost associated with each travel link. The selected route would theoretically be the expected route in the statistical sense, that is, the expected travel time or money cost would be the sum of the travel times or money costs over each possible route weighted by the probabilities of taking that route.

System Boundaries

When defining a system, it is necessary to identify its boundaries and to characterize it as open or closed. There is no easy way to set boundaries on recreation systems for benefit estimation purposes. Clearly, in order to estimate the benefits of a particular park, we have to include in the system all the counties likely to send visitors to it. These counties can be identified more or less arbitrarily, on the basis of the type of park under consideration. Suppose we want to estimate the benefits of some park (A). The relevant population zone might be included inside the

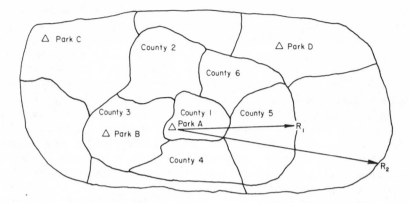

Figure E-1. Recreation-System Boundaries

radius R_1 shown in Figure E-1. This zone might typically have a radius of 75 to 100 miles and be comprised of 10 to 20 counties.

It was noted that accessibility to recreation is a key factor in determining the number of visits ascribed to a particular county per unit time. Thus, for each county near the border R_1, in considering the share of its total visits captured by Park *A*, we need to include in the system all the parks that might conceivably be visited by its residents. For instance, residents of County 6 have the option of visiting Park *D* as well as Park *A*. (In fact, Park *D* is closer than Park *A*.) This consideration has the effect of extending the system boundary from R_1 to R_2 in Figure E-1. The distance (R_2-R_1) might again be on the order of 75 to 100 miles. Thus, in this case, our recreation system has a radius of anywhere from 150 to 200 miles. Of course, this boundary applies only to the type of park considered in this study. Other, more attractive sites have entire states or groups of states within their boundaries. Some national parks, for instance, have a market area that includes practically the entire United States.

In this discussion, we are obviously dealing with an open system in that, however the system is defined, visitors can come into it from outside, and visitors from inside the system can leave it to visit parks outside. We certainly cannot account for everybody. There will inevitably be seepage into the system and leakage out of it.

Conceptual Model for Estimating Recreation Benefits

The total-willingness-to-pay approach to the estimation of primary recreation benefits advocated in this study involves the construction of demand curves for specific recreation sites by utilizing data on actual recreation trip patterns over real world recreation systems. By developing a functional relationship between trip-making and corresponding measurable travel costs, the effects of added costs on participation and trip patterns can be inferred, and a demand curve to estimate benefits can be developed by making the appropriate assumptions. In addition to cost, such a demand function needs to incorporate all other factors which affect demand and subsequent values. A three-stage model for doing this was developed by Battelle. The model has the capability of estimating the benefits of any set of new or existing parks in a region. The three stages or components of the model are discussed separately. However, as shown later, these components can be combined neatly into a single equation for purposes of parameter estimation.

The three components of the recreation model are (1) the participation component; (2) the distribution component; and (3) the benefits component (Figure E-2).

Participation Component of the Recreation Model

The participation component of the model estimates participation, in terms of party visits per unit time, from selected counties to the system recreation facilities. A party is considered to be made up of people visiting the park as a group (including groups of only one person). The party does not, by definition, have to travel in a car. Loosely stated, the basic hypothesis to be tested is that participation in outdoor recreation for any county is a function of (1) population in the county; (2) selected socio-economic characteristics of the population such as age and income; and (3) opportunity to participate or, equivalently, accessibility of outdoor recreation. That is,

$$N_i = f(P_i, S_i, O_i), \tag{1}$$

where

N_i = Total number of recreation trips per unit time from County i
P_i = Population of County i
S_i = Socioeconomic characteristics of residents of County i
O_i = Accessibility of outdoor recreation opportunities to residents of County i.

Postulating the relevant factors affecting participation in outdoor recreation is only the first step in the analysis. The next steps involve (1) seeking ways of measuring the relevant variables; and (2) hypothesizing the structure of the model, that is, the way in which these factors are combined to yield a plausible explanation of recreation behavior.

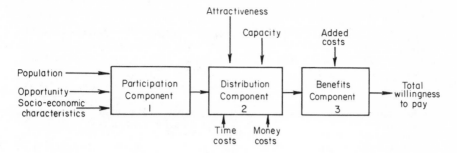

Figure E-2. Schematic Three-stage Battelle Recreation Model

Measurement of Variables. The measurement of the variables in Equation (1) ranges from easy to difficult—the measurement of population is straightforward and the measurement of accessibility is very difficult.

Accurate national population counts are made by the Bureau of the Census every 10 years, and more frequently, under special circumstances for small areas of the United States. When needed, it is possible, using a variety of proven techniques of varying sophistication, to estimate population for interdecile years and project population into the future for small units such as counties using Census data and such additional information as records of births and deaths and school enrollment. For the purpose of this study, Battelle does believe it necessary to develop elaborate population estimates. The population estimates used are essentially compromises among estimates by (1) standard population trend extrapolations of Census data, (2) a major market research group;[1] and (3) various state planning agencies.

The variability in outdoor recreation participation among people possessing different socioeconomic characteristics has been the subject of much speculation and investigation by researchers. Just as people of different ages have different tastes and preferences in music, clothing, and hair styles, so do they seem to have different tastes and preferences for outdoor recreation activities. Other social characteristics for which different recreation behavior patterns have been observed are sex, religion, education, race, residential location, and family status. Economic factors, such as employment status, income, and occupation, which govern the means whereby one is able to exercise his recreation choices, are also important in shaping the demands for various kinds of recreation outputs.

It appears that not only the numbers of people participating but also the frequency of participation can differ dramatically among different socioeconomic classifications. To illustrate these differences, Table E-1 partially summarizes 1965 National Recreation Survey Data related to socioeconomic effects affecting swimming participation. Participation in

Table E-1

Outdoor Recreation Participation Data Classfied by Socioeconomic Characteristics

Socioeconomic Characteristics		Swimming		
		Percent Participating	Percent of Swimmers	Average Days per Participant
Total, U.S.	All	48	100	14.3
Age	12–17	84	27	23.2
(years)	18–24	74	20	12.5
	25–44	55	37	11.0
	45–64	26	15	9.5
	65+	6	1	10.3
Race	White	50	94	14.7
(color)	Nonwhite	27	6	7.9
Residence	Metropolitan	52	70	15.0
(place)	Nonmetropolitan	40	30	12.8
Income	Under 3,000	21	8	11.0
(annual	3–6,000	45	27	12.1
dollars)	6–8,000	55	21	12.9
	8–10,000	63	13	15.1
	10–15,000	64	19	17.2
	15–25,000	72	6	19.4
	25,000+	68	2	19.6
Education	8 or less	15	14	6.8
(years)	High school 1–3	34	17	8.8
	High, 4	44	40	11.1
	College, 1–3	55	13	12.4
	College, 4+	60	16	13.1
Size of Family	1–2	27	17	10.3
(persons)	3–4	24	42	14.6
	5+	60	41	15.7
Geographic	New England	61	9	18.5
Area	Middle Atlantic	52	21	14.2
(BOR region)	East North Central	46	20	13.1
	West North Central	41	7	14.6
	South Atlantic	46	14	13.1
	East South Central	31	4	14.4
	West South Central	40	6	11.7
	Mountain	39	3	14.1
	Pacific	59	16	15.7

Source: Bureau of Outdoor Recreation, U.S. Department of the Interior, "The 1965 Survey of Outdoor Recreation Activities," October 1967.

swimming seems to be increasing with income, education, and family size and decreasing with age; rates also differ with respect to color, place of residence, and geographic area.

This brief socioeconomic analysis serves to illustrate the basic premise that people with similar backgrounds and characteristics might be observed to behave similarly, and this behavior very often deviates significantly from national and regional norms. It is not necessary to know the reasons why people with different socioeconomic characteristics behave differently, only that they do. We need to know this in view of the fact that the population unit under consideration is a county. Each county in even a very small region would be expected to be composed differently with respect to the relative sizes of its various socioeconomic subgroups. Thus, widely different county-by-county recreation behavior patterns may emerge. We would want to be able to understand and account for these differences as much as possible in any explanatory model.

There is usually a high degree of multiple correlation among these socioeconomic factors. For instance, it is not difficult to imagine that there is a high degree of positive intercorrelation among age, income, and education. That is, people with high incomes are typically older and better educated than people with low incomes. In the case of high multiple correlation among variables, the model need only include one of the variables together with the assumption that the correlation found to exist in the past will hold into the future.

In previous sudies, perhaps the most neglected factor affecting participation in outdoor recreation is the accessibility of recreation opportunities. Apart from any socioeconomic considerations, people confronted with different opportunities will tend to do different things. It stands to reason that people will engage primarily in those activities for which there is opportunity to do so. And, they will likely partake of the opportunities in amounts related to the ease with which it is possible to make use of them. An extreme example of this postulate concerns the outdoor recreation activity of skiing. The participation rate in skiing (that is, trips per person per year) is probably quite high in Colorado relative to Indiana because there is little opportunity for skiing in Indiana.

The research problem in the past has been one of devising a relevant measure of opportunity accessibility since it is not directly observable in nature. Both the number and location of available recreation sites must be considered jointly in the construction of an accessibility variable.

Several possible measures of accessibility can be derived, ranging from extremely crude measures to fairly complex computational procedures. We let the subscript i refer to the "i^{th}" county and j refer to the "j^{th}" recreation site. Let opportunity accessibility of County i be denoted by Z_i. The location of an opportunity will be defined by the necessary time, trouble, and money required to reach it. For convenience, we call this total cost and denote by C_{ij} the total cost to a resident of County i who visits Recreation Site j. Assume M parks comprise the system.

The simplest measure of accessibility would be to define it as the total number of recreation sites within a given total cost zone, C_o, around the population center. This amounts to weighting opportunities by a step function of cost. Symbolically, this composite measure can be expressed as:

$$Z = \sum_{j=1}^{M} \gamma_{ij},\tag{2}$$

where

$$\gamma_{ij} = 1 \text{ for } C_{ij} \leq C_o$$
$$= 0 \text{ for } C_{ij} > C_o$$

The two big drawbacks of this measure are that (1) there is no systematic method for determining C_o (indeed, it seems unreasonable that such a sharp cutoff value exists); and (2) all opportunities within the cost zone defined by C_o (and elsewhere) are assumed equally preferable.

To eliminate the problem created by Item (1), an alternative cost function might be given by

$$f(C_{ij}) = \beta C_{ij}^{-\alpha}.\tag{3}$$

This function assigns to each opportunity a unique value which represents the propensity of recreationists to visit the site in the absence of all other sites. The negative power on cost represents the elasticity of visits with respect to cost and allows for this cost function to be nonlinear. (Elasticity in this case would be technically defined as the "percentage change in visits for each percentage change in cost.")

To overcome Item (2), we can weight each opportunity by its attractiveness to the population. It is unreasonable to assume that all parks are equally preferable to recreationists. Each park is unique, owing to the fact that different activities are offered, the quantity and quality of the facilities differ, and the scenic and environmental features are unlike. Without delving more at this time into how we determine the attractiveness weights, which will be denoted for Park j by A_j, we introduce these improvements to obtain

$$Z_i = \sum_{j=1}^{M} A_j f(C_{ij})$$

$$= \beta \sum_{j=1}^{M} A_j C_{ij}^{-\alpha}.\tag{4}$$

Though this equation is more realistic than either Equation (2) or Equation (3), the components of the accessibility variables (that is, A and C) are difficult to measure and the parameters (that is, α and β) need to be estimated statistically. More will be said about these measurements and estimation problems later.

Alternative Approaches to the Participation
Component of the Recreation Model

(This section, which is of considerable importance to those interested in further improvements in model construction for recreation, will be of limited interest to those readers primarily concerned with the results from use of the model rather than the model itself. Those readers may wish to turn directly to the section entitled "The Participation Model Used in This Study.") It is not enough to postulate that certain variables or factors might be useful in explaining differences in outdoor recreation participation levels among various population groups. It is equally, if not more, important to postulate how these variables or factors are combined to yield a plausible and realistic model of recreation behavior. Again, we have a spectrum of possible models ranging from the very simple to the very complex. Four basic models were considered for this purpose, each involving different degrees of aggregation over population groups and activities. These are discussed below.

Model I. This model, the one commonly in use by various governmental agencies, is motivated by the belief that the single most important determinant of the number of visits emanating from a population center is the number of people living there, and that the product they seek is general recreation as opposed to individual activities. Hence this, the simplest conceivable model, involves aggregation of overall population subgroups and outdoor recreation activities. There is also an implicit assumption that participation rates are independent of accessibility.

The model can be expressed symbolically as

$$N_i = f(P_i) = rP_i \, , \tag{5}$$

where

N_i = Number of visitors from County i for all recreation activities per unit time

r = Participation rate in outdoor recreation activities (visits per capita per unit time)

P_i = Number of people residing in County i.

This model requires only one parameter estimate, that is, the participation rate for all outdoor recreation activities. Objections to this model are: (1) the recreation sites being considered in this study each offer only a subset of the total number of conceivable outdoor recreation activities and this subset varies among individual parks; (2) differences in participation among people with different socioeconomic characteristics are not explicitly recognized; and (3) the relationship between participation and opportunity is not included. Thus, a great deal can be gained by (1) disaggregation into more homogeneous population groups (Model II); (2) disaggregation into activity categories (Model III); and (3) introduction of opportunity or supply variables (Model IV).

Model II. It was observed in Table E-1 that recreation participation varies across various socioeconomic groups. Since individual counties are known to differ considerably with respect to overall socioeconomic characteristics, this phenomenon must be included in the model. The symbolic representation of this model is

$$N_{is} = f(P_{is}) = r_s P_{is} \,, \tag{6}$$

where

N_{is} = Number of visitors from County i in Socioeconomic Category s for all outdoor recreation activities per unit time

r_s = Participation rate for outdoor recreation activities in Socioeconomic Category s

P_{is} = Number of people of County i in Socioeconomic Category s.

This model requires estimates of the participation rates for outdoor recreation in each socioeconomic category and of the size of the various socioeconomic subgroups within the total population.

Model III. We are primarily interested in estimating participation for various subsets of the total set of outdoor recreation activities. Modifying Model II, we get a model of the following type:

$$N_{isk} = r_{sk} P_{is} \,, \tag{7}$$

where

N_{isk} = Number of visitors from County i of Socioeconomic Class s in Activity Group k per unit time

r_{sk} = Participation rate for Socioeconomic Class s in Activity Group k

P_{is} = Number of people in County i in Socioeconomic Category s.

There is a serious problem of classification, however, in implementation of this model.

The participation component is to be linked up with a component that distributes visits to system recreation facilities. The point has been made that any given recreation system is comprised of sites, many of which offer different activity mixes (the total activities offered themselves being some small subset of all outdoor recreation activities). On any one outing, people tend to partake in several different complementary activities. If we summed the number of occasions of swimming and picnicking, for instance, this total would far exceed the number of people who participated in these activities. The problem lies in setting up mutually exclusive activity categories. It has been concluded that this cannot be done except in the rare cases where only one activity can be undertaken at a given site.

To overcome this difficulty, we assume that on a particular multiple activity recreation trip certain of the activities are primary (dominant) and other activities are secondary (subordinate). In some cases, of course, we have codominance—that is, two or more activities attract equally. In other words, we assume that every visit is motivated primarily by the desire to participate in one or more activities, and other activities are participated in but are less likely to motivate the visit. Each visitor can be classified according to the activity that dominates his visit. An example of a dominant subordinate relationship might be fishing and boating, that is, the desired activity is fishing, and boating, being complementary, is of secondary interest. When this person selects a site, he evaluates it primarily on its fishing qualities and not its boating qualities. An example of codominance might be swimming and water skiing. It should be clear that each person is not expected to have the same dominant subordinate relationships, but only that we can establish such relationships for each individual.

These considerations lead to extending the model as follows:

$$N_{isk}^T = r_{sk}^D P_{is} + r_{sk}^S P_{is}$$

$$= r_{sk}^D P_{is} + \sum_j \sum_{k' \neq k} (r_{sk}^D P_{is}) \mathrm{prob}(k/k')j$$

$$= r_{sk}^D P_{is}\left[1 + \sum_j \sum_{k' \neq k} \mathrm{prob}(k/k')_j\right], \tag{8}$$

where

N_{isk}^T = Total number of visitors from County i in Socioeconomic Category s in Activity Group k per unit time

r_{sk}^D = Participation rate in Activity Group k as dominant activity for Socioeconomic Group s

r_{sk}^S = Participation rate in Activity Group k as secondary activity for Socioeconomic Group s

Prob $(k/k')_j$ = Probability of participation in k as secondary activity given participation in activity k' ($\neq k$), assuming existence of facilities for k for Park j.

As the participation model becomes more realistic and useful, the data requirements become more substantial. In addition to previous data, two additional requirements for this model are: (1) a measure of activity preferences cross-classified by dominant and subordinate activities as well as population attributes; and (2) data on activities participated in on each trip classified by park.

It remains to factor in the effects of recreation opportunities on participation.

Model IV. One of the simplifying assumptions of the first three models is that the participation rates in various activities do not vary with access to recreation facilities. This assumption is at odds with the theory of demand, according to which participation (that is, consumption) should increase as the price of recreation decreases. As more and more recreation facilities become available in a region, the price of recreation goes down for people residing in the area of the new sites. This concept has been advanced before under a different guise. Access effects are of interest not only for theoretical reasons but also because they constitute an important planning variable.

Using the final form of Model III, we first assume that the participation rate for an Activity k for a Socioeconomic Group s as a dominant activity is a function of the degree of access to that activity as measured by Equation (3). That is,

$$ r_{sk}^D = f\left(\sum_{j=1}^{M} A_{sjk} C_{ij}^{-\alpha} \right) = \beta \left(\sum_{j=1}^{M} A_{sjk} C_{ij}^{-\alpha} \right)^{\eta}, \qquad (9) $$

where β and η are behavioral parameters.

We now get, as an extension of Equation (8),

$$ N_{isk}^T = \beta \left(\sum_{j=1}^{M} A_{jsk} C_{ij}^{-\alpha} \right)^{\eta} P_{is} \left[1 + \sum_{k} \sum_{k' \neq k} \text{prob}(k/k') \right]_j. \qquad (10) $$

This model as it stands is obviously difficult, if not impossible, to estimate. First, we need to estimate three parameters (α, β, η) in this nonlinear equation. Next we need to derive attractiveness indexes for individual activities for different socioeconomic groups. We then need to derive a cost function which incorporates both money cost and time cost. Participation rates for dominant activities need to be estimated. Finally, the probabilities of participating in a particular activity as a secondary activity need to be derived. This feat is complicated by the fact that dominant subordinate relationships vary with individuals and small groups of individuals such as families, and data would be needed at a very disaggregate level. A simplified version of Equation (10) seems desirable.

Participation Model Used in the Study

Rather than work with the extremely complicated model given by Equation (10) to predict county participation in individual activities, a model was formulated to estimate participation in the total subset of recreation activities under investigation. In the model, the breakdowns into individual activities occur after all trips have been distributed. The model, as envisioned at this point, estimates, for a particular county, total participation in the seven selected activities that will take place in some combination at all available multiple-purpose public recreation areas (swimming, picnicking, boating, hiking, fishing, sightseeing, and camping). At this point we will not have estimates of participation by individual activities—we will have estimates only of the total number of recreation trips in the selected activity subset per unit time emanating from the county. This is all made possible by the introduction of a simplification in the park attractiveness measure (taken up in detail later). Suffice it to say at this time that the attractiveness measure, rather than being activity-specific, is a composite measure reflecting the combined quantity and quality of all activities offered at a site attractive to people in a particular socioeconomic category. By introducing this change which, in effect, eliminates the need of an Activity Index k, Equation (10) reduces to

$$N_{is}^T = \beta \left(\sum_{j=1}^{M} A_{js} C_{ij}^{-\alpha} \right)^{\eta} P_{is},$$ (11)

where

N_{is}^T = The total number of trips per unit time for recreation of the type under study from County i in Socioeconomic Group s per time period

P_{is} = Number of people in County i in Socioeconomic Group s

A_{js} = Attractiveness of Recreation Area j to Population Group s

C_{ij} = Cost of travel from County i to Park j

α, β, η = Parameters to be estimated.

This is the form of the participation hypothesis, in its simplest form. It basically says that participation in outdoor recreation is a joint function of population and opportunity accessibility. Note that opportunity accessibility for socioeconomic groups has formerly been defined as

$$Z_{is} = \sum_{l=1}^{M} A_{ls} C_{il}^{-\alpha}.$$

This equation has certain desirable mathematical properties. Since modifications would be made before parameters were estimated, these properties are better taken up after the complete model has been formulated.

Distribution Component of the Recreation Model

Once the estimates of participation in outdoor recreation are available for all counties in the system, the trips are distributed to all the parks in the system, with these distributions being governed by tradeoffs between attractiveness and costs of alternative recreation areas. The distributional laws can best be understood by means of examples. From a discussion of these examples, an operational definition of attractiveness would evolve.

If a group of individuals is confronted with the choice between two recreational areas—Site 1 and Site 2—both equal in cost or accessibility, it would be expected that those that prefer Site 1 will generally go to 1 and those that prefer Site 2 will go to 2. Thus, we end up with a certain fraction of total visitors at each park. The park drawing the highest fraction of visitors in this case can be considered to be the more attractive from the point of view of the group as a whole (but not, of course, from the point of view of each individual). For example, if 75 percent of all visitors went to 1 and the remaining 25 percent went to 2, 1 can be considered for this purpose to be 3 times as attractive as 2. This observation forms the basis of our operational definition of attractiveness: Relative attractiveness of one park with respect to another to any population group is the ratio of their relative visits over some period of time, other things equal. It is implied by this definition that the relative attractiveness of two parks is stable over time. This does not necessarily mean that the same ratio of visitors will be observed each and every time the distribution of visits is examined, only that the average ratio, suitably measured over a sufficient time span, is constant if no changes are made in park facilities. That the same people visit the same parks over and over again is *not* implied. It does not matter who visits which park as long as the ratio of visits of one park with respect to another is stable.

It is a rare case when two or more alternatives are equally accessible to any population group. When sites are not equally accessible, relative attractiveness cannot be estimated simply by observing the way the population groups split up between two parks. For instance, Park 1 may be located 10 miles away from the population center, and Park 2 may be located 100 miles away. If the parks were equidistant, perhaps more people would, on the average, visit Park 2. According to our operational definition of attractiveness, Park 2, would be more attractive than Park 1 by an amount equal to the ratio of their respective visits. Yet when they are not equidistant, as they are in our latter case, Park 1 might well out-draw Park 2. The reason for this, of course, is that the rewards available at Park 2 are not worth the cost incurred in getting there for marginal visitors who would go to Park 2 if the two parks were equidistant. Thus, accessibility and attractiveness must be considered jointly in the model. It follows that visits are directly related to attractiveness and inversely related to some function of cost.

To derive an expression for estimating the distribution of visits from any Population Center i to any recreation area, it may thus be assumed that the expression for the relative number of visits to Sites 1 and 2 from any Population Center i can be constructed by noting that $v_{i1} \approx A_1 C_{i1}^{-a}$ and $v_{i2} \approx A_2 C_{i2}^{-a}$. That is, the number of visits to Park 1 from Population

Center i (V_{i1}) is directly proportional to its attractiveness (A_1) and inversely proportional to some function of its cost of access to residents of Population Center i (C_{i1}). From this, letting u be the constant of proportionality, we can write

$$\frac{v_{i1}}{v_{i2}} = \frac{u(A_1/C_{i1}{}^\alpha)}{u(A_2/C_{i2})^\alpha} = \frac{A_1/A_2}{(C_{i1}/C_{i2})^\alpha} . \tag{12}$$

In the case of equal costs, the expression reduces to

$$v_{i1}/v_{i2} = A_1/A_2 , \tag{13}$$

which implies that visitors will distribute according to the relative attractiveness of the two sites, as was shown before. If the attractiveness of both parks is equal, an equal number of visitors will be drawn to each site (that is, $v_{i1}/v_{i2} = 1$); if attractiveness is unequal, visitors will split up in the ratio of their group preferences.

In the case of equal attractiveness, the expression becomes

$$v_{i1}/v_{i2} = (C_{i1}/C_{i2})^\alpha , \tag{14}$$

which says that visitors will split up according to some function of relative cost. If the attractiveness is not equal, that is, if $A_1 \neq A_2$, visitors will split up according to Equation (12).

As Equation (12) gives only the relative number of visits to two areas, modifications must be made in order to get an explicit expression for the number of visits to each park. We can rewrite Equation (12) as

$$v_{i1} = \frac{A_1/A_2}{(C_{i1}/C_{i2})^\alpha} v_{i2} , \tag{15}$$

and define

$$N_i = v_{i1} + v_{i2} , \tag{16}$$

where N_i represents the total number of visitors emanating from Population Center i to be distributed. Since only two parks are here considered to be in this system, we can write

$$v_{i1} = \frac{A_1/A_2}{(C_{i1}/C_{i2})^\alpha} (N_i - v_{i1}) . \tag{17}$$

Rearranging terms, we get

$$v_{i1} = N_i \left(\frac{A_1/C_{i1}^\alpha}{\sum\limits_{j=1}^{2} A_j/C_{ij}^\alpha} \right)$$

and

$$v_{i2} = N_i \left(\frac{A_2/C_{i2}^{\alpha}}{\sum\limits_{j=1}^{2} A_j/C_{ij}^{\alpha}} \right). \tag{18}$$

Equation (18) comprises the distribution model for allocating trips from Population Center i to each of two parks.

Equation (18) would hold for any two parks in any larger system. That is, replacing the subscripts 1 and 2 by j and j' to denote arbitrary parks, and assuming that there are M parks in the system changes Equation (12) to

$$v_{ij} = N_i \left(\frac{A_j/C_{ij}^{\alpha}}{\sum\limits_{j=1}^{M} A_j/C_{ij}^{\alpha}} \right)$$

$$v_{ij'} = N_i \left(\frac{A_{j'}/C_{ij'}^{\alpha}}{\sum\limits_{j=1}^{M} A_j/C_{ij}^{\alpha}} \right). \tag{19}$$

Thus, for any Arbitrary Park, q,

$$v_{iq} = N_i \left(\frac{A_q/C_{iq}^{\alpha}}{\sum\limits_{j=1}^{M} A_j/C_{ij}^{\alpha}} \right). \tag{20}$$

In the manner of Equation (20), the number of visitors to any arbitrary park in the system is obtained by replacing the numerator with the appropriate attractiveness-cost ratio. The denominator, which is the accessibility variable, remains constant for each such calculation. The total number of visitors to any park, j, per unit time, V_j, is obtained by summing Equation (20) over all N population centers. That is,

$$V_q = \sum\limits_{i=1}^{N} \left[N_i \left(\frac{A_q/C_{iq}^{\alpha}}{\sum\limits_{j=1}^{M} A_j/C_{ij}^{\alpha}} \right) \right]. \tag{21}$$

Equation (21) is the means whereby the visitation at a particular park is estimated, provided total participation is known for each population center. This type of formula, particularly the portion enclosed by parentheses, is commonly known as a gravity model. This model has been successfully applied elsewhere for describing various other types of transportation and travel phenomena. A justification and derivation of the model, such as that provided in the preceding pages, has never been provided, however, in the recreation literature or any other literature.

The distribution model is intuitively appealing as well as theoretically sound. The model assumes that there is both a pulling force—attractiveness —and a repelling force—cost—which jointly affect the decision by members of society to visit or not to visit a particular park. The exerting force of any park can be expressed as the ratio of its attractiveness to its cost. If we add all these sources we get the total exerting force of the entire system. The fraction of total visitors drawn to one particular park is given by the ratio of its attractiveness-cost ratio to the total exerting force of the system. Thus, the fraction of total visits drawn must be between 0 and 1. In addition, the model ensures that all visitors—no more, no less—are distributed.

Benefits Component of
the Recreation Model

The benefits component of the model constructs demand curves for recreation sites by operating on earlier equations through the cost term C, suitably defined. We assume for now that the cost term includes the correct relationship between money cost and time cost.

To summarize developments up to this point, the system boundaries for the park(s), new or existing, for which benefits are to be estimated are established. The participation model estimates the number of total recreation visits per unit time emanating from all counties in the system; the distribution model then distributes these trips to all the system recreation sites and estimates the total number of visitors at each site. Assuming that t is the time unit of the model and L is the duration of the planning horizon, the model is run a total of L/t times. For each of these t time periods we have one point on the demand curve for each site—the total visits to be realized under the existing prices, be it zero or otherwise. An arbitrary increment of money cost is then added. The model estimates the effect of this added cost by recalculating the travel patterns under the new costs and estimates the new number of visitors to the site(s). This is done for each time period to establish a second point on the demand curve. Then, costs are incremented and a third point on the demand curve is established. This process continues until costs become high enough to drive the number of visitors to zero. The recreation-site demand curve is now completely defined for each time period. The areas under the curves are calculated and benefits are estimated by discounting this time stream of benefits at an appropriate discount rate. The whole procedure works in the following way.

We have assumed for a given recreation site a function of the type

$$v_{ij} = f(C_{ij}, P_i; x_1, x_2, \ldots, x_n), \tag{22}$$

where $(x_1, \ldots, x_n)$ denote relevant demand and supply variables. We have further hypothesized a linear relationship between visits to Site j from Population Center $i(v_{ij})$ and population (P_i). Thus, we can write Equation (22) as

$$\frac{v_{ij}}{P_i} = f(C_{ij}; x_1, x_2, \ldots, x_n). \tag{23}$$

We now have a relationship between per-capita visit rates and the variables affecting it. The number of visits to Park j under the initial price (V^0) is estimated by multiplying the population of each population center by its visit rate as given by Equation (23) and adding the visits from all counties together. This is given by

$$V^0 = \sum_{i=1}^{N} f(C_{ij}; x_1, x_2, \ldots, x_n)P_i. \tag{24}$$

Assume that we now impose an additional cost of $\triangle C$ on each visitor. The visit rate for all counties will change as given by the demand function, Equation (23). Whereas under the original costs we had V^0 total visits, we now end up with

$$V^1 = \sum_{i=1}^{N} f(C_{ij} + \triangle C; x_1, x_2, \ldots, x_n)P_i \tag{25}$$

total visits, where

$$V^1 \leq V^0. \tag{26}$$

Continuing our analysis in this way, letting $C^k = k\triangle C$, we add increments of cost until the number of expected visitors has been reduced to zero. The resulting function is shown in Figure E-3. If we assume that the costs are added in the form of fees, then Figure E-3 is interpreted as the demand curve for the recreation site.

The area under the curve can then be calculated by approximation methods. This area is taken to be the total economic value to society of the recreation services provided by the site for the time period under consideration.

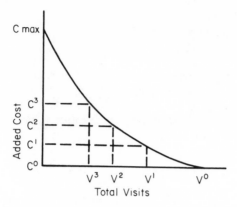

Figure E-3. Construction of Recreation-Site Demand Curve by Benefits Component of the Model

Combining the Three Model Components

Up to this point, the participation, distribution, and benefit components of the proposed recreation model have been given separately. We can now show how these components of the model collapse into one equation—an equation that can be used for practical application in estimating recreation use of different sites.

The equation for predicting the number of visitors emanating from any population center, omitting the socioeconomic subscript, was given as:

$$N_i = \beta \left(\sum_{l=1}^{M} A_l / C_{i1}^{\alpha} \right)^{\eta} P_i \,.$$

With slight changes in notation, the trip-distribution model was given as:

$$v_{ij} = N_i \frac{A_j / C_{ij}^{\alpha}}{\displaystyle\sum_{l=1}^{M} A_l / C_{il}^{\alpha}} \,.$$

Substituting the former equation into the latter equation results in:

$$v_{ij} = \beta \left(\sum_{l=1}^{M} A_l / C_{il}^{\alpha} \right)^{\eta} P_i (A_j / C_{ij}^{\alpha}) \left(\sum_{l=1}^{M} A_l / C_{il}^{\alpha} \right)^{-1}$$

$$= \beta P_i \left(\sum_{l=1}^{M} A_l / C_{il}^{\alpha} \right)^{\eta-1} (A_j / C_{ij}^{\alpha}) . \tag{27}$$

The concept of socioeconomic influences in participation can be reintroduced by adding the socioeconomic subscripts, where appropriate. We also eliminate the need for the division signs in the model by noting that the parameter α can be allowed to take on negative values. The model now becomes (for convenience $\eta = n - 1$)

$$v_{ijs} = \beta P_{is} A_{js} C_{ij}^{\alpha} \left(\sum_{l=1}^{M} A_{ls} C_{ij}^{\alpha} \right)^{\eta} . \tag{28}$$

The model as given here thus estimates participation and distributes it simultaneously. Benefits are estimated by adding costs through the cost terms and constructing demand curves. Thus, we have all the previous concepts embodied in Equation (28). This, then, is the basic structure of the recreation model as proposed.

Needed Refinements

Certain refinements need to be made to make the model operational. These refinements are of three types: (1) a more precise definition of the cost function; (2) a way of estimating attractiveness of parks; and (3) the introduction of saturation effects.

The Cost Function

In the preceding discussion total cost has been denoted by C. It has also been noted that the correct cost function includes the costs in money, time, and perhaps driving. As the measurement of benefits necessitates the postulation of the effect on visit rates of changes in money costs alone, without changing the other costs, a formulation of the total cost is desired which allows separately for the effects of time and money cost.

The problem could be managed if it were possible to estimate the effects separately, that is, estimate an equation with each cost component treated as a separate variable. It would then be possible to change one without the others. Unfortunately, such a procedure is usually impossible. The difficulty is that travel costs in money outlay and time are very highly correlated, making it impossible to separate the effect of one from the other; short travel times are associated with small money outlays and long times with large expenditures. While some variance is introduced by toll roads, which increase money costs on some routes above those on other routes equally time-consuming, the range of differences is still far too narrow in nearly all cases. This correlation has the effect of severely narrowing the observation range to a narrow band over the range of money and time costs.

Though it appears that one could use either cost or time as an explanatory variable—a procedure that has been used in all previous applications of the method proposed herein—this is not satisfactory for present purposes. The need is to predict changes in behavior when moving from one observed point to a point that takes us out of the observation space.

The problem can be illustrated with reference to Figure E-4. It can be assumed that two points are observed: a visit rate resulting from trips made both over a short distance requiring 1 hour and over a longer one requiring 4 hours. In the first instance, Figure E-4 suggests a visit rate of 20 visits per capita, with a time cost of 1 hour and a money cost of 1 dollar. In the latter, a rate of two visits per capita for a trip requiring 4 hours and 4 dollars is indicated. While other observations may have been made, they all would have been in the observation space given by the area centered on the diagonal on which these two points lie.

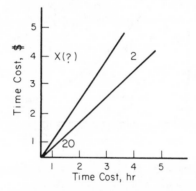

Figure E-4. Illustration of the Difficulty of Incorporating Separable Time and Money Costs in the Recreation Model

The benefit estimate, as previously outlined, requires an estimate of points such as X, in Figure E-4. In this case, an estimate is needed for a trip requiring the same time as that of the rated 20 visits per capita, and the same money cost as that of the rated 2 visits per capita. The question we ask is: "If people in the nearer county were required to pay an added $3 over the $1 they now pay, by what amount would their visit rate be reduced?"

In all past applications the answer has been assumed that upon increasing the cost, the new visit rate would fall to that of the more distant county —in this example, the county with costs of $4. However, this second county also has time costs of 4 hours. It cannot be expected therefore that the visit rate would fall all the way to that of this second county. This would imply that only money costs have relevance and that time has none —a notion demonstrably wrong.

People do make trade-offs between time and money costs. That is, they —taken as groups—will visit at similar rates with various levels of money and time costs. Therefore, if some plausible assumption can be made about the nature of the relevant trade-off functions for recreation trips, a better estimate of the visit rates can be made. A possible function is indicated in Figure E-5, using data parallel to that in the earlier illustration.

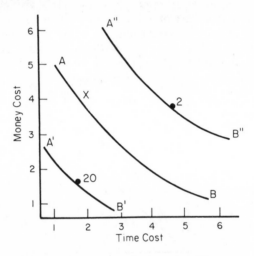

Figure E-5. Trade-off Function Between Time and Costs

This curve is drawn convex to the origin. It is also drawn through Point X, but it can be thought of as but one of a family of such curves, one of which goes through the point of 20 visits per capita (A', B') and one for 2 visits per capita (A'', B'').

As the observed data can be obtained only from a narrow cone up the diagonal of the diagram, it is necessary to postulate a slope for the curve in order to estimate visit rates outside of the observed points. The slope convex to the origin indicated in Figure E-6 is predicted on the generally observed phenomenon of diminishing marginal or incremental effect of a small amount of time or money on the trip decision as the size of the time or money expenditure already invested increases. That is, the effect on the visit rate of adding one single minute to a trip is likely to be greater for trips of ten minutes than for trips in which people already travel say ten hours. In the latter case another minute is insignificant, but it may not be in the former.

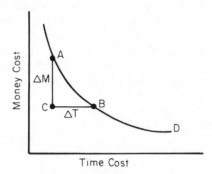

Figure E-6. Marginal Effects of Money and Time Cost

In the same way an additional 10 cents would likely not appreciably affect rates for trips that already involve large expenditures compared to those involving but small amounts. If these presumptions hold, the curves will exhibit the convexity indicated. This can perhaps be seen with reference to Figure E-6. The slope of the line is given by the change in money (ΔM) over the change in time (ΔT). All points on the curve indicate equal visit rates by definition. Therefore, a small negative change in money multiplied by the effect of this change would have to be offset by a positive change in time such that the added time increment multiplied by its incremental effect just equals the negative effect of the other. That is, in terms of Figure E-6, a change from A to B can be thought of as a negative change from A to C and a positive one from C to B. This can be written as $-\Delta M$ (marginal effect of M) $= \Delta T$ (marginal effect of T). This can be rewritten, after cross-multiplying:

$$-\frac{\Delta M}{\Delta T} = -\frac{\text{Marginal Effect of Time}}{\text{Marginal Effect of Money}}. \tag{29}$$

The left side of the equation is simply the slope of the curve at any point. By definition then, the slope at any point is equal to the relative marginal effects of time and money.

Referring back to the notion of decreasing marginal effects of time and money, it can be seen that at Point A the marginal effect of time is relatively large, as not much time has already been involved here, and the marginal effect of money is relatively small, as considerable money is already expended at this point. This, then, indicates a fairly large negative slope at this point. At Point D, the reverse is true. The marginal effect of time is relatively small and that of money is large, indicating a smaller negative slope. The convexity to the origin is thereby indicated.

This formulation of a trade-off function between time and money costs provides the basis for replacing the C terms of earlier equations by some function of both money and time. The function is constrained by the requirement that the slope be convex to the origin. This can be done by simply using a new variable defined as (CT) where C is money cost and T is time cost. Each quantity can be measured in any convenient units. This formulation insures convexity. Thus, for an observation of 1 hour and $1 costs, the visit rate value can be taken as (1×1) if time is measured in hours or, alternatively, (60×1) 60 if time is measured in minutes.

The use of this new variable permits an estimate to be made of the visit rate for any point in Figure E-6 by simply changing C, without changing T, and then calculating the new visit rate.

The issue of how to treat these problems of time and cost, tentatively resolved in the discussion above, is highly critical in formulating the ultimate benefit estimates. To explore these issues in more complete detail, Battelle has examined the benefit estimates resulting from a different shape of the curve reflecting this trade-off.

Attractiveness and Saturation Effects

The problems of (1) estimating the numerical values of park attractiveness and (2) modifying the model to incorporate saturation effects are considered jointly since, as will be shown, overcrowding is, in essence, an attractiveness component. This hypothesis results in replacing the *"A"* item in the previous equations with an interaction term between facilities and crowds. Justification of this replacement is given below.

In the absence of saturation (that is, when all parks in the system have unlimited capacity), it would be easy to estimate attractiveness indirectly, employing a few very reasonable assumptions. For two parks, j and j', the relative number of visits per unit time from County i can be expressed as before:

$$\frac{v_{ij}}{v_{ij'}} = \frac{A_j/A_{j'}}{(C_{ij}/C_{ij'})^\alpha}.$$

By a simple transportation of terms, one gets

$$A_j/A_{j'} = (V_{ij}/V_{ij'})(C_{ij}/C_{ij'})^\alpha. \tag{30}$$

We now have the attractiveness ratio of two parks, j and j', expressed in terms of relative visits and relative costs from County i. This gives a convenient way of making pairwise comparisons for estimating attractiveness, if Equation (30) is assumed to hold for all i and all j. Since, for some particular time period, we presumably have means of measuring the v's and now, hopefully, the C's, it would be possible to collect data on the variables on the right side of this equation. This leaves the attractiveness ratio and the parameter a to be determined.

One critical assumption is needed in order to do this. This has already been provided. Note that it has been implicity assumed, through the distribution component, that populations in each county will rank parks in exactly the same way. That is

$$A_j/A_{j'} = \frac{v_{ij}}{v_{1j'}}\left(\frac{C_{1j}}{C_{1j'}}\right)^{\alpha} = \frac{V_{2j}}{v_{2j'}}\left(\frac{C_{2j}}{C_{2j'}}\right)^{\alpha} = \ldots = \frac{v_{Nj}}{v_{Nj'}}\left(\frac{C_{Nj}}{C_{Nj'}}\right)^{\alpha}. \quad (31)$$

This may seem a heroic assumption, but it is certainly a testable one. To be sure, this assumption may be too broad. The assumption we really want to make here is that every socioeconomic group will rank parks in the same way. This could be handled by adding the socioeconomic subscripts as before.

By virtue of Equation (31) we now have N observations with two parameters to estimate. It would be possible, with the proper transformations, to obtain simultaneous least-squares estimates of $A_j/A_{j'}$. An alternative trial-and-error procedure which accomplishes the same result is as follows:

All pairs of parks can be examined for each population center (i). The analysis is conducted for several values of a within some reasonable range, and that value is chosen which minimizes the variance in estimates of $A_j/A_{j'}$ across counties. For parks where no v_{ij}'s are observed, transitivity is assumed. That is, if Park A is preferred to Park B and Park B to Park C, then Park A is preferred to Park C.

After completing the analysis for the system of $(N \times M)$ size, we end up with estimates of A_j/A_j for all i and j. Since attraction indexes are used, Attraction A_1 of Park 1 can arbitrarily be set equal to 1 and the attraction of Parks 2, 3, . . . , N can be computed by taking $A_j = 1/A_1/A_j = A_j/A_1$ for $j = 2, . . . , M$.

This imputation approach for deriving attractiveness indexes is an indirect measurement method in that, when done, we do not really know what it is we have measured. About all we can say about these numbers is that we have imputed a set of attractiveness indexes based on revealed preferences. Our objective should be to determine attractiveness components, that is, what factors must be considered and weighed in order to use a direct measurement method for determining attractiveness. This question is particularly relevant for parks in the planning stages where it is of course impossible to impute attractiveness without knowing what factor and factor weightings comprise it. It is useful for planning purposes to know what features of parks people desire and the relative importance of each. It is suspected that for the parks under consideration in this study, attractiveness is some composite function of the number of, kind of, and quality of facilities offered. A function of the following type suggests itself:

$$A_j = \sum_{k=1}^{K} u_{1k}(x_k)u_{2k}(x_k)\gamma_k , \qquad (32)$$

where

A_j = Attractiveness of Park j

u_{1k} = Utility of having Activity x_k available

u_{2k} = Utility of quality of Activity x_k

γ_k $\begin{cases} 0 \text{ if Activity } x_k \text{ not offered} \\ \\ 1 \text{ if Activity } x_k \text{ offered.} \end{cases}$

When considering various activities, each combination of activities must be treated as a separate activity, because not only does each individual activity have its own weight, but each combination has its own weight. It is implied here that the weights for two or more activities are not the sum of the weights of the individual activities comprising it—the aggregate weights could be more or less, depending on the particular activities under consideration.

Facilities alone will define attractiveness as long as everyone is free to visit any park he wishes to at any time—that is, as long as capacity is unlimited. Anyone who has attempted to find an empty picnic table at his favorite park on a hot summer Sunday will attest that the capacity constraint is indeed significant. There is difficulty in defining capacity since it is so elastic in the case of parks, but this does not rule out any adverse effects from crowding as perceived by park users. Overcrowding has two main effects on visit patterns: (1) a diversion effect whereby crowded parks are bypassed in favor of less attractive and perhaps lightly used parks; and (2) a repelling effect whereby people stay home rather than go for an outing. Thus, both participation and distribution are affected.

The attraction of parks can no longer be considered a function only of facilities—saturation effects need to be included also. This can be accomplished in the model by letting the term A be represented by an interaction between some index of facility quantity and quality, denoted by I, and a saturation term representing the degree of crowdedness of the park. If we let S_j be the capacity of Park j and V_j be the number of visitors to Park j, we can let the ratio S_j/V_j be an index of crowdedness. Symbolically, we have, for any park (j), for some time period (t),

$$A_j^t = f[I_j, (S_j/V_j)^t] . \qquad (33)$$

The time superscript is inserted to indicate that, with the crowdedness term included, attractiveness is a dynamic rather than static concept—the overall appeal of a park to the general public changes over short time spans. We can now rewrite the distribution model, omitting the time superscript, but adding the relevant parameters, as

$$\frac{v_{ij}}{v_{ij}} = \frac{[I_j(S_j/V_j)]^\eta / [I_j'(S_j'/V_j')]^\eta}{(C_{ij}/C_{ij}')^\alpha}. \qquad (34)$$

Note that we now assume that distribution is such as to achieve equality between the $[I_j(S_j/V_j)]/[I_j'(S_j'/V_j')]$ among all counties. The implication here is that, in agreement with common sense, crowds are more tolerable in more attractive parks than they are in less attractive parks.

One could argue that this formulation does not insure that capacity constraints will be satisfied over any time period. This argument, although correct, is not a valid criticism of the model. It has been mentioned that capacity is a very elastic concept and cannot be determined precisely. This model, rather than ensuring that some undefinable capacity constraint be satisfied, imposes that crowds are spread among all parks rather than becoming concentrated in a few highly attractive places.

Incorporating this formulation in the participation model gives

$$N_i = \beta P_i \left[\sum_{l=1}^{M} I_l(S_l/V_l) \right]^\eta. \qquad (35)$$

Under certain values of the parameters, to be discussed in a following section, the model will have the ability of driving participation down as parks become overcrowded and, as crowdedness decreases, driving participation up. Thus a feedback mechanism in the form of oscillations in participation is introduced which respond to crowds, or lack of them, in the system.

It is interesting to note that once equilibrium has been attained, the composite measure $I_j(S_j/V_j)$ can be estimated by the method of the previous section. It then remains to factor out the separable facilities and crowdedness effects.

The Complete Model

It is possible now to state the final form of the basic recreation model and to present the basic hypotheses to be tested in terms of parameters to be estimated.

The Recreation Equation

By incorporating the last modifications into the fundamental recreation equations and converting the Greek letters which represent true parameters into a vector $B = (b_0, b_1, \ldots, b_9)$ which represents estimated parameters yields

$$V_{ijs} = b_0 P_{is}{}^{b_1} I_j{}^{b_2} (S_j/V_j)^{b_3} (M_{ij}{}^{b_4} + b_5 T_{ij}{}^{b_6})^{b_7}$$

$$\times \left[\sum_{l=1}^{M} I_{ls}{}^{b_2} (S_l/V_l)^{b_3} (M_{il}{}^{b_4} + b_5 T_{il}{}^{b_6}) \right]^{b_7 b_8}. \quad (36)$$

This is the recreation model. Though the model is ominous when seen in final form, it is not so ominous when it is seen to be evolved from a few basic behavioral premises.

This model is intrinsically nonlinear. That is, no transformations can be imposed on this model to allow the parameters to be estimated by ordinary linear techniques. Nonlinear estimation methods must be used.

Tests of Hypotheses

Many behavioral postulates underlying the final model structure are given by Equation (34). Most of these have been discussed. These postulates are confirmed or refuted by the values of parameters that result from applying some statistical parameter-estimation routine. For the model to be plausible —that is, gives sensible answers—each parameter must fall within a predetermined plausibility region. If the parameter falls outside its specified region, the behavioral postulate implied by it must be rejected even though the model might have good predictive power. This is a very discriminating testing procedure. Table E-2 gives the regions within which each estimated model parameter must fall to be accepted.

The principal hypothesis to be tested is that the model is useful in estimating recreation travel flow. The hypothesis would be accepted only if all nine parameters fell within their acceptance regions.

It should be clear that the model evaluation problem is not a simple one. There is no simple objective measure of success or failure. Thus, two criteria—feasibility and predictive power—have to be considered jointly.

Transient Use

The method described here is applicable for estimating what is termed local use—that is, visitors originating from home, traveling to the park, and returning home again the same day. In addition to local use, another kind of use is frequently found at any given recreation site. These are the transients who do not live in the region in which the park is located. Transients are those travelers who are either on a long vacation trip and

Table E-2

Parameter Feasibility Regions

Parameters	Feasibility Region	Implications of Parameters Outside Region
b_0	$b_0 > 0$	(1) If $b_0 < 0$, negative number of visitors generated.
		(2) If $b_0 = 0$, no visitors are ever generated.
b_1	$b_1 > 0$	(1) If $b_1 < 0$, visits get fewer as population increases.
		(2) If $b_1 = 0$, visits are independent of population.
b_2	$b_2 \geqslant 0$	If $b_2 < 0$, visits get less as attractiveness increases.
b_3	$0 \leqslant b_3 \leqslant 1$	(1) If $b_3 < 0$, overcrowding enhances park appeal.
		(2) If $b_3 > 1$, no equilibrium visitor distribution is reached.
b_4	$b_4 \geqslant 1$	(1) If $b_4 < 0$, visitors increase as money cost increases.
		(2) If $0 \leqslant b_4 < 1$, convex cost-time indifference curve not obtained.
b_5	$b_5 > 0$	If $b_5 \leqslant 0$, money cost and time cost not substitutable.
b_6	$b_6 \geqslant 1$	(1) If $b_6 < 0$, visitors increase as time cost increases.
		(2) If $0 \leqslant b_6 < 1$, convex cost-time indifference curves not obtained.
b_7	$b_7 < 0$	(1) If $b_7 = 0$, visits are unrelated to total cost.
		(2) If $b_7 > 0$, visits increase as total cost increases.
b_8	$-1 \leqslant b_8 \leqslant 0$	(1) If $b_8 < -1$, visits decrease as accessibility increases.
		(2) If $b_8 = -1$, visits are independent of accessibility.
		(3) If $b_8 > 0$, no equilibrium visitor distribution is reached.

stop at a park to eat their lunch, or Sunday drivers out on a park-hopping tour. The level of this use at a particular park is related primarily to the proximity of that park to major highways. It is difficult, if not impossible, to include transient use explicitly in the model as developed for day users. In addition, it is hypothesized that the willingness-to-pay of transients, since they typically make only limited use of park facilities, is considerably less than for day users who stay considerable lengths of time and accrue more benefits. It could in fact be reasonably argued that if the price of the park were set at market, most transients would not be willing to pay this price. However, it seems reasonable that they would be willing to pay something. In view of these difficulties, and in view of the fact that the number of transients at parks in the mid-Atlantic region is typically a small percentage of total use, it was decided to include them as a constant percentage of day use and assume that the shapes of the demand curves were identical for both local and transient use.

The Need for Separate Day Use and Camper Models

The recreation equation [Equation (36)] is, in general, applicable to all types of recreation travel—however, one or more of the parameters might vary depending on the type of trip under consideration.

The three main visitor types are (1) day users (those who leave their home, visit the park for less than a day, and return home); (2) overnight users (those who remain in the park one or more nights); and (3) transients (those who drop in for a few minutes or hours as part of an extended trip). Each group has different amounts of time available, interests, motivations, and behavioral characteristics. There is reason to believe that the parameters of the model would be different for each group. Campers exhibit different travel patterns than day users. Campers characteristically travel further, stay longer, and spend more money than day users. The parameters of the model should reflect these differences. It follows that if we could plot trip attenuation from a population center for both day users and campers, the day use curve would probably indicate a rapid drop in visits with time, whereas the campers might exhibit a curve exhibiting a threshold below which participation would be low, at which participation would reach a maximum, and after which participation would diminish, but at a slower rate than for day use. It seems in order to estimate parameters separately for these three groups. However, this was not possible in the case of transients and only day users and campers were analyzed in detail.

F   A Political Theory for Institutional Analysis

Vincent and Elinor Ostrom *

Wildlife, fishlife, oil, groundwater, lakes, streams, and the atmosphere are all examples of common pool resources. Particular problems occur in the utilization and management of these kinds of resources whenever the following conditions are present: (1) ownership of the resource is held in common; (2) a large number of users have independent rights to use of the resource; (3) no one use can control the activities of other users or, conversely, voluntary agreement or willing consent of every user is required in joint action involving the community of users; and (4) total use or demand upon the resource exceeds the supply.

As soon as these conditions prevail, efforts of any one user to increase his supply of the resource from a limited common pool leads to an adverse effect on others. Any one user, following the economic calculus, will attempt to increase his utilization of the resource until his marginal costs equal his marginal benefits without taking into account the spillover costs he creates for other users. Some spillover costs will be felt by others who wish to utilize the common supply for the same purpose and must now pay higher costs to do so. Other spillover costs will be felt by users who wish to utilize the common supply for different purposes and may now be excluded from doing so or may have to pay higher individual costs to do so.

Since spillover costs may be extensive, each user may be led to adopt strategies which produce high costs for others while acting in relation only to his own private costs and private benefits. In addition, each user may be led to overinvest in developments concerned with his own individual use. Intense competition for the limited supply will result unless institutional arrangements require all users to take spillover costs, as well as their own individual costs, into account when making decisions regarding the utilization of the common resource. Such competition may force some users out of existence and may produce extraordinarily high costs in the continued utilization of the resource.

A consequence of utilizing the rule of willing consent in the development of a common pool resource will be the relative lack of attention to investment in projects which would provide a common benefit. Even though total benefits exceed total costs, the specific benefit to any single user will rarely exceed the total costs. Thus, the single user is not apt to invest in projects of common benefit without some arrangement requiring other

* This theory was developed by Vincent Ostrom and Elinor Ostrom, both of whom are Professors of Political Science at Indiana University, and was prepared in this form by them especially for inclusion in this program.

benefited individuals to contribute their share. Consequently, many potential spillover benefits will not be realized.

Therefore, sole reliance upon the rule of willing consent in the development of a common pool resource may lead to overinvestment in facilities for private use and benefit, and simultaneously, underinvestment in facilities for joint benefit. Investment in facilities to utilize a lake system as a fishery is an example of this paradoxical problem of achieving optimal decisions regarding the use of common pool resources. Unless institutional facilities are established to change the structure of incentives and deterrents, individual fishermen will be led to overinvest in fishing gear and boats for their private use while underinvesting in the development of the common fishing stock.

Not all uses of a common pool resource need to be competitive. An increase in the quality of water of benefit to a municipal water supply may also be of benefit to those who use the same resource for other purposes such as fishing and recreation. The construction of a flood control dam on a river system, if properly designed, may also create joint benefits in the production of hydroelectric power and in recreational use of the reservoir. However, the building of that dam may create costs for the use of that resource for such things as navigation and fishlife.

Once a competitive common pool situation develops, users relying upon a basic decision rule of willing consent, and following the economic calculus, will be led to accelerate their competitive race with one another for the limited supply. Individual users may be led to adopt any or all of the following patterns of conduct: (1) to conceal or to minimize recourse to essential information; (2) to ignore adverse effects on the resource in the conduct of his own enterprise; (3) and/or to follow a hold-out strategy in relation to other parties drawing upon the same resource pool.

Since information about how much of the resource any one individual is using may lead others to try to limit his activities, an individual may attempt to conceal information about his own use pattern. Further, an individual may ignore the general consequence of his personal actions. A single user, changing only his own actions so as to take into account the social costs he creates, will seldom have much effect on the whole system unless all other similar users also change their behavior in the same way. Thus, any effort to force any one individual in a competitive common pool situation to take into account the social costs he creates leaves that person at a disadvantage in competition with others without fundamentally altering the excess demand being made upon the common pool resource. It is only when efforts can be made to change the cost calculus of all similar actors that a real social benefit can be achieved without undue harm to any single individual. If efforts are made to gain voluntary agreement by all users to change their production patterns so as to reflect the total costs of their activity, some individuals will be led to adopt hold-out strategies. If all users except a few reduce their demands upon a limited common pool resource, this increases the supply available to those who hold out and refuse to go along with a voluntary arrangement. If any user is free to terminate a voluntary agreement regarding the utilization of a resource, most users will be unwilling to enter into such an agreement. Few individuals are willing to make considerable personal sacrifices if the primary benefit will go to the least cooperative joint user.

It therefore is necessary to forego the use of willing consent as the sole decision rule in order to gain a capability to enforce joint decisions on all parties. Solutions to common pool problems inevitably involve some form of public organization to assure collective decisions that can be enforced against all users. This requires recourse to the coercive capabilities inherent in government authority.

Evolution of a Monopolist

One solution of the common pool problem is to allow intensive competition to run its course until one individual group acquires a monopoly position over the resource. Range wars over control of waterholes in the West illustrate the tragic drama that can accompany such a solution. The exercise of monopoly power may permit efficient development of a common pool resource but, more likely, it will create serious problems at other junctures in the economic process.

Resource development predicated upon a negative or zero-sum game is an emphatically uneconomic venture. It is the fear that all may lose in the long run that stimulates individuals to seek some alternative solution to common pool problems.

Appeal to Existing Public Agencies

The existence of intensive competition does provide an incentive for a community of affected users to seek some common solution to their problem. The reduction of spillover costs for the community of users by adopting policies that take each others interests into account represents a potential benefit to be captured. This benefit can be captured if a community can have recourse to appropriate institutional arrangements normally found in the public sector. The potential benefit in the form of reduced spillover costs and increased spillover benefits can be conceptualized as a potential political (or community) surplus available for capture by those who develop institutional arrangements to accomplish this purpose.

A public jurisdiction may already exist with an appropriate boundary and range of capabilities for dealing with some common pool problems. In such a case, articulation of demand for new services from such an agency would probably involve less time, money, and energy than development of a new arrangement. Often, however, the boundaries of existing public agencies are either too small or too large.

Jurisdictions which are too small can encompass only a portion of the individuals affected by the development of a common pool resource. Such jurisdictions can only effect changes in relationship to the citizens included within its boundaries. The citizens of that jurisdiction may pay to reduce their own spillover costs only to be forced to bear the spillover costs created by others.

Jurisdictions which are too large may include persons who have no direct interest and are, thus, extraneous to solving the common pool problem. If extraneous populations become involved in the management of a common pool resource (such as paying a general tax to support some activity of local benefit only), they may require some benefits or side payments from those directly benefited as the price of participation. The presence of extraneous interests creates incentives to make side payments in the form of log rolling or vote trading in order to sustain necessary voting coalitions. Side payments for sustaining voting coalitions represent a cost in political decision making, and in the most aggravated form may raid the public treasury as a common pool resource.

Therefore, wherever a governmental jurisdiction represents constituencies of a significantly different magnitude than those affected by the provision of a particular public service, an increasing bias toward inefficient solutions can be expected.

Even where an existing public jurisdiction has boundaries that include the relevant public affected by utilization of the common pool resource, it may not possess the necessary decision-making capabilities. Management of a common pool resource normally requires extensive investment in information-gathering facilities concerning the nature and extent of the resource and the demand or patterns of use, and an assessment of the likely consequences of alternative management programs. In addition, a jurisdiction may need to possess a complex mix of taxing and pricing powers to distribute the costs of the enterprise in a way that will lead toward an optimal pattern of use. It may also need police powers to enforce various regulations designed to achieve the desired result.

Formation of New Collective
or Public Enterprises

If individuals adversely affected by spillover costs in their utilization of a common pool resource, or desiring to invest in projects producing spillover benefits, cannot find an appropriate solution available among existing public jurisdictions, they may then contemplate forming a new collective or public enterprise. Establishment of new institutional arrangements in the public sector involves costs of two types: potential deprivation costs and potential opportunity costs.

Potential Deprivation Costs. Whenever authority for making decisions about joint activities is moved into the public sector, someone may be forced to abide by a decision with which he does not agree. The creation of such a public jurisdiction means that someone can be deprived of his free choice when a collective public decision is made. Deprivations may be relatively low if the enterprise adopts a policy only slightly at variance with the preference of those who do not agree. However, deprivations may at times be relatively great if severe sanctions are necessary to insure conformance to a collective decision.

At the time of constituting a new enterprise, individuals cannot predict all of the decisions that will be made in the future. However, for given voting rules, individuals can predict the likelihood of their concurrence with decisions. For example, if only one person, or a small subset of individuals, will make all important and binding decisions, those affected can predict disagreement with many decisions. In such a case, affected individuals may expect to suffer high deprivation costs. In contrast, if majority votes will be taken on all issues, those affected can predict that they have a chance of agreeing with at least half of the decisions. Therefore, potential deprivation costs would be lower under majority rule than under a rule allowing only a few to decide for all. Potential deprivation costs continue to decrease as the proportion of individuals from a given group that must agree prior to taking an authoritative decision increases. If unanimous agreement is necessary before actions can be taken, potential deprivation costs would be zero, although the cost in time and effort to reach such agreement could be extremely high.

In Figures F-1 through F-3, the vertical axis measures total costs or benefits derivable from collective action. The horizontal axis represents the proportion of individuals required to agree to a decision before action can be taken.

Figure F-1 illustrates the relationship between voting rules and potential deprivation costs as discussed above.

Potential Opportunity Costs. When people must agree to a decision before action can be taken, time, money, and effort that could be used for other purposes must be devoted to gaining agreement. While engaged in the attempt to reach a joint decision, the opportunity to take other actions may pass by and, if the decision-making process is long and involved, other opportunities to invest for joint benefit may be lost. Therefore, time, money, and effort devoted to collective decision making, and the opportunities foregone while deliberations are in process, can all be conceptualized as potential opportunity costs.

Figure F-2 illustrates the relationship between potential opportunity costs and different voting rules. If only one person were required to make legitimate decisions for a public enterprise, opportunity costs would be minimal. As the number of persons required to agree increases, so do the time, money, and effort that must be invested to reach a collective decision, thus increasing the opportunity costs. As unanimous consent is approached, opportunity costs become very high.

Total Costs of Collective Decision Making. If it were not for the very high opportunity costs associated with unanimous consent, profit-maximizing entrepreneurs would attempt to organize private enterprises to deal with common pool problems. On the other hand, if potential deprivation costs were not so high when decision-making authority is given to one or a few individuals, public enterprises might be managed by a small oligarchy or a dictator. It is evident, then, that the most economic and acceptable method for dealing with common pool resource problems lies somewhere between the extremes of unanimous consent and dictatorship.

The results obtained when taking both cost functions into account are illustrated in the combined, U-shaped cost curves of Figure F-3. If the deprivations that can be imposed by a prospective public enterprise are limited, while the opportunity costs are relatively high, the low point of the total cost curve will occur towards the low side of the proportion of persons required to agree in making an authoritative decision (Figure F-3a). If the deprivations that can be imposed are very high and the opportunity costs are relatively low, the low point will occur where a relatively large proportion must agree in making a decision (Figure F-3b). If the potential deprivations and potential opportunity costs are relatively balanced, the low point will fall approximately in the middle range of potential voting rules (Figure F-3c).

Whatever the shape of the total collective decision-making curve, if a portion of that curve lies below the benefit level, a net benefit can be achieved through some form of collective action. The Lines B-B′ in Figure F-3 represent the potential net benefit which could be derived by reducing spillover costs to a community of joint users, investing in projects producing spillover benefits, or a combination of both. These lines represent the present value of the flow of future benefits derived from collective action less the flow of future production costs involved in undertaking such a program. These benefit levels indicate that a political surplus is available, the amount that can be realized being dependent upon which decision rules are adopted.

Consequently, if full information were available concerning the shape of these curves, most affected individuals would be willing to agree to the formation of a new public enterprise when the proposed decision rules involve less cost than the benefits to be derived. In Figure F-3, any decision rules which required between Q and Q' of the affected individuals to agree to a major decision prior to action would result in an increase in

179

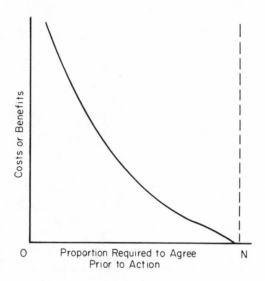

Figure F-1. Potential Deprivation Costs

Figure F-2. Potential Opportunity Costs

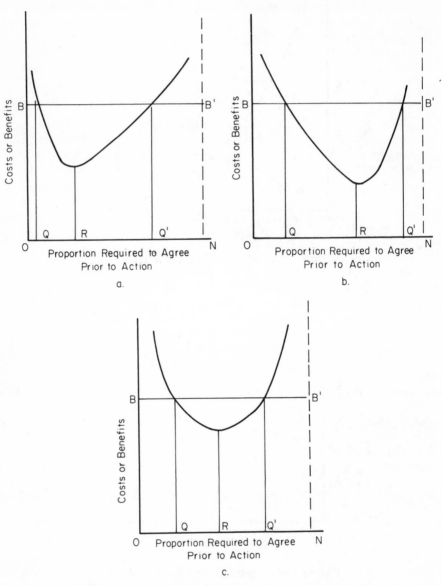

Figure F-3. Total Collective Decision-making Costs

net benefits to the community. Social benefits would be maximized if the decision rule represented by the low point on the total-costs curve was adopted. In each case, the rule producing maximum benefit has been labeled R. If the optimal rule were proposed, individuals affected by the organization of a new enterprise would maximize their net benefits through its establishment even though (1) they would be forced to abide by some future decision to which they did not agree; and (2) they would also pay some opportunity costs.

However, notice that the optimal decision rule (R) varies in each of the three cases illustrated in Figure F-3. Individuals faced with differently shaped total cost curves might attempt to devise separate enterprises to prevent each type of social cost or to gain each type of social benefit of individual action. Alternatively, individuals might constitute one enterprise for dealing with all issues but utilize different decision rules for each set of issues.

Lack of a Permanent,
Long-Run Solution

The dynamics of our society dictates that decisions and constraints be viable. What is established as an optimal solution to a common pool resource problem at any point in time can never be considered as a permanent solution. Some of the factors which mitigate against the permanence of a solution include: (1) the boundary of those affected by spillover costs may change; (2) individuals may obtain better or new information which shows a need for changes in arrangements; and (3) new technologies may be developed that create or prevent spillovers.

The Boundary Problem. Some natural resources subject to common pooling may be very large (such as the Great Lakes). The system itself may also be composed of a large number of subsystems. Human utilization of the resource will lead to the establishment of many common pools within common pools where individuals at one location may not be affected by actions taken at another location. Establishing a new public agency to deal with a particular common pool problem may create new spillover costs for others outside its boundary who were previously unaffected. One way for a public agency to reduce spillover costs within its own boundaries is to dispose of some spillover costs beyond its boundaries. Chicago, for example, was able to reduce pollution in Lake Michigan by diverting the flow of its sanitary system into the Mississippi River system, but at the cost of increased diversion of water from the Great Lakes, which could have an adverse effect on the system.

If a public agency is physically located in relationship to a natural resource system so that it can dispose of spillover costs beyond its boundaries without adversely affecting the utility of the resource for its own citizens, it can be expected to do so. Reduction of spillover costs created by public agencies may become particularly difficult when resource systems are larger than the more general units of government, such as states, provinces, or nations. Regulation of rivers which pass through a number of different states frequently generates long conflicts among the states and sometimes requires recourse to the U.S. Supreme Court, to Congress, and to Federal executive agencies. The problem of finding long-run solutions to common pool problems is complicated still further in the case of any resource system which extends beyond the boundaries of a single nation.

As a population affected by the development of a vast common pool resource increases, the boundaries of public decision-making arrangements capable of dealing with common pool problems may become inadequate. New jurisdictions may be needed, but not necessarily just the creation of larger and larger districts. Gigantic jurisdictions responsible for comprehensive planning for a common pool resource may be unable to envision and realize many of the particular benefits desired by small groups of affected individuals utilizing various aspects of the complex system. Consequently, it may be desirable to create a structure of incentives and deterrents among numerous agencies functioning in a public enterprise system so the spillover costs created by each public agency will be taken into account in its relationships with other agencies.

When each set of interests is articulated through the structure of some agency, a variety of mutual interests can be handled by negotiation as long as some known judicial or political remedy is also available should negotiations fail. Through negotiated contractual relationships, agencies may be able to develop exchange agreements to reduce the total level of spillover costs in the larger resource system and/or to enter into joint investment in facilities which could produce a higher level of joint benefit from the resource pool. Such negotiation of contractual relationships among special and general governmental agencies at all levels may be facilitated by the threat of eventual takeover of certain functions by a larger political jurisdiction if existing agencies cannot reach a satisfactory arrangement. Court actions have also been utilized to goad public agencies into reaching agreements. However, the process of negotiating mutually agreeable arrangements may involve relatively high decision costs reflected in time, effort, and opportunities foregone.

The Uncertainty Problem. If individuals solving problems through the political process possessed perfect information, they would be capable of reaching optimal solutions. However, individuals attempting to solve common pool problems face a number of uncertainties, many related to the complexity of the natural resource system itself. These uncertainties may be further clouded by biasing in the way information is presented to those concerned with constituting new institutional arrangements.

As noted, there is a general tendency for a party involved in a common pool problem to conceal information about his own utilization patterns for fear that this information may be used against him. This tendency to conceal information may be exaggerated by underestimation of future demands for joint benefits. If it appears that the common benefit will be provided in any case, an individual may understate his own demand in hopes of reducing his share of the cost. If the common benefit is provided as a public service, each individual will benefit no matter what share of the costs he bears. The lack of a *quid pro quo* relationship in regard to the provision of many common pool benefits leads to a systematic downward biasing of information regarding demand by users of collective services who do not control production decisions.

On the other hand, there are those who envision the possibilities of joint gain through collective action, and assume the entrepreneurial initiative in putting together a public enterprise. Individuals who function as public entrepreneurs will expect to (1) have access to better than average information about the nature of the common pool resource; (2) be more than proportionately harmed if joint action does not occur, or more than proportionately benefitted if collective action does occur; and (3) have a high expectation of functioning as an official decision maker in any new institutional arrangement.

A portion of the expected deprivation costs perceived by most individuals involved in a constitutional process may be considered as potential income by public entrepreneurs. Deprivation of others in the form of taxes, fines, and assessments enables entrepreneurs to undertake the activities they think are important. Deprivation costs may also provide a source of personal income to a public entrepreneur. Since those who function as public entrepreneurs are more assured of a significant voice in most decisions, they are less concerned about future adverse decisions. Thus, public entrepreneurs will have an expected deprivation-cost curve which is lower than that of others involved in a constitutional process, the difference being the potential income to the public entrepreneur.

On the other hand, public entrepreneurs perceive opportunity costs more directly than many others involved in a constitutional process. They are the ones who spend large amounts of time and effort trying to reach agreements, have greater access to information, and are more aware of the opportunities foregone while individuals argue about what should be done. The expected opportunity-cost curve of public entrepreneurs will usually lie above that of others involved in the constitutional process, the difference being potential costs impinging more directly on public entrepreneurs than on others.

As a result of the difference in perception between public entrepreneurs and others involved in a constitutional process, the curve for the public entrepreneurs' expected total collective decision-making cost would resemble in shape Line 1 in Figure F-4, while curves for the expected total collective decision-making cost of others might look like Line 2. The optimal decision-making rules from the perspective of the public entrepreneur would be *G*, while the optimal decision rules from the perspective of others affected would be *U*. At *G*, those affected by the provision of a collective benefit will realize a net return from collective action equal to *EF*. At *U*, the net return from collective action would be equal to *RT*, while public entrepreneurs will pay higher costs than others, that is, equal to *ST*.

This divergence between the expected costs of affected individuals in general, and those of public entrepreneurs in particular, will lead public entrepreneurs to stress opportunity costs and to discount deprivation costs in any discussion of a common pool problem. They will tend to exaggerate the crisis nature of problems. By stressing that a crisis exists, entrepreneurs may be able to shift the curve for the estimated total decision-making cost of most individuals upward to the right. This has the effect of moving the estimated optimal decision rule to the left or toward a less inclusive

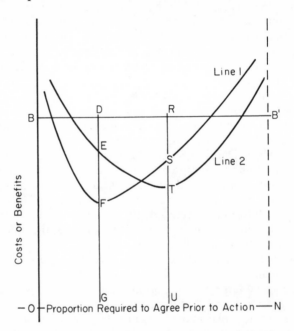

Figure F-4. Divergence Between Expected Total Collective Decision-making Costs of Public Entrepreneurs and Other Affected Individuals (Line 1 = Estimated Total Decision-Making Costs: Public Entrepreneurs; Line 2 = Estimated Total Decision-Making Costs: Others Affected)

rule. If public entrepreneurs are successful in leading individuals to believe that opportunities will be foregone unless authority is given to a small proportion of those affected to make decisions rapidly, a decision rule delegating responsibility to a limited proportion of affected individuals may be adopted. Affected individuals may later feel that the deprivation costs of such a decision are too high and may attempt to change the basic rules.

Development of New Technology. Uncertainty created by lack of knowledge about a complex physical system, plus the problem of systematic biasing of certain kinds of information, may be complicated still further by technological innovations that create new opportunities and constraints requiring alteration of existing institutional arrangements. The introduction of new industrial processes (such as the production of thermonuclear power) may produce new spillover costs which previous institutional arrangements did not anticipate, or, on the other hand, technological advances may enable individuals to undertake projects previously considered unfeasible. For example, introduction of Coho salmon into the Great Lakes represents a technological innovation in the development of Great Lakes fisheries. To realize the economic potential of this new development may, however, require institutional arrangements to control chemical residues from hard pesticides such as DDT.

*Some Special Problems
of Institutional Change*

Since a relatively optimal solution to the common pool problem at one point in time cannot be considered to be a permanent solution, there is need for generalized institutional arrangements to facilitate a continuing process of learning and readjustment. It is apparent that individuals affected by common pool problems can benefit through the provision of reliable and accurate information by a disinterested third party. In addition, such a third party may be able to formulate alternative actions which take into account the mutuality of interests involved in a common pool problem, as well as the individual interests of each partisan. Individuals dealing with a high degree of uncertainty can make more optimal decisions if there is an independent source of information without systematic biases. To avoid such bias, an independent source of information should not have responsibility as a producer or user of water services related to the common pool resource other than that of producing reliable information.

Institutions of government are formalized ways of arranging for the availability of third party offices when individuals are not able to reach a satisfactory resolution of a conflict. Courts have frequently appointed impartial, disinterested third parties to supply information on utilization of the common pool resource. For example, the Conservator of the Thames, established approximately a century ago, was charged with the responsibility of providing information concerning the effect on the river of proposed utilization of diverse kinds. In the absence of formalized governmental institutions, parties to conflicts may act jointly to employ the services of a third party intermediary. Lawyers have traditionally performed such services. In an era of collective bargaining in labor management relations, the services of labor mediators are often jointly procured by labor and management. Similar services have been provided by private engineers to agencies concerned with the development of groundwater management programs.

In addition to the need for an impartial source of information regarding a common pool resource, individuals trying to achieve optimal development will be aided by some form of pricing or taxing. While not so easy to establish as with packageable private goods, pricing has several beneficial consequences. To the extent that the price (or tax) reflects social costs (foregone opportunities for others), it encourages the individual user to take the social costs of his actions into account. Pricing mechanisms add a form of cost calculus to the multitude of individual decisions made concerning the use of a common pool resource.

The use of a pricing or taxing mechanism also provides needed revenue to undertake joint projects to prevent costly spillovers or to create beneficial ones. In addition, pricing mechanisms increase the amount of information available concerning the demand that individuals have for certain types of services. A form of a *quid pro quo* relationship ensures that those who want to utilize a resource have a definite way of articulating that demand. It also ensures that those who want to play the role of the holdout are discouraged from that strategy. If the price is right, the potential holdout has nothing to gain by such a strategy.

Thus, while there cannot be a permanent solution to the institutional problems associated with common pool resources, a mix of institutional facilities may enable individuals affected by these problems to learn from past experience and to continue changing institutional patterns toward more optimal outcomes. This mix will contain a large variety of public agencies of differing boundaries and powers. It will contain sources of reliable, unbiased information. It will most likely also include the utilization of diverse forms of pricing or user charges where applicable.

Notes

Notes

Chapter 1
The Need for Research

1. U.S. Department of the Interior, "Analysis of Water and Water Related Research Requirements in the Great Lakes Region," report of the Council on Economic Growth, Technology, and Public Policy of the Committee on Institutional Cooperation, to the Office of Water Resources Research, Washington, June 1968, p. 81.

Chapter 2
The Research Program

1. R. T. Jaske and J. L. Spurgeon, "A Special Case: Thermal Digital Simulation of Waste Heat Discharge," in *Water Research* (New York: Pergamon Press, 1968).

2. For a detailed elaboration of the basis for these ideas, see David Easton, *A Systems Analysis of Political Life* (New York: John Wiley & Sons Inc., 1965).

3. For a somewhat dated but still largely valid description of this parallel structure in the area of water resources, see R. C. Martin, G. S. Burkhead, J. Burkhead, and F. J. Munger, *River Basin Administration and the Delaware* (Syracuse: Syracuse University Press, 1960), Chapter 3, "The Parties at Interest."

4. Robert K. Davis, *The Range of Choice on Water Management: A Study of Dissolved Oxygen in the Potomac Estuary,* published for Resources for the Future Inc. by Johns Hopkins Press, Baltimore (1968).

5. U.S. Army Engineer District, Basin Studies Branch, *Potomac River Basin Report* (Baltimore, February 1963).

6. Davis, *Choice on Water Management,* p. 8.

7. United States Department of Interior, Federal Water Quality Administration, Great Lakes Region, *Lake Erie Report, A Plan for Water Pollution Control,* August 1968.

8. Ibid., p. 84.

9. For a discussion of such strategies see Arthur Maas, et al., *The Design of Water Resource Systems* (Cambridge, Massachusetts: Harvard University Press, 1962), Chapter 10.

10. *Lake Erie Report,* p. 86.

Appendix A
Water Pollution in the Great Lakes Basin

1. Most of the material in this Appendix was taken from a Battelle—Northwest Research Report on "Great Lakes Restoration—Review of Potentials and Recommendations for Implementation," to the Commission

190

on Marine Science, Engineering and Resources, Washington, D.C., June 17, 1968.

2. Clair N. Sawyer, "Basic Concepts of Eutrophication," *Journal Water Pollution Control Federation* (May 1966), pp. 737–744.

3. K. M. Stewart and G. A. Rohlich, *Eutrophication: A Review,* report to the State Water Quality Control Board, State of California (1967).

4. Alfred M. Beeton, "Indices of Great Lakes Eutrophication," *Proceedings: Ninth Conference on Great Lakes Research* (Publication No. 15, Great Lakes Research Division, The University of Michigan, 1966), pp. 1–8.

5. E. J. Martin and L. W. Weinberger, ibid.

6. Sawyer, "Basic Concepts."

7. E. J. Martin and L. W. Weinberger, *Eutrophication.*

8. A. V. Kneese, *Water Pollution: Economic Aspects and Research Needs* (Washington, D.C.: Resources for the Future, Inc., 1962).

9. "Report on Commercial Fisheries Resources of the Lake Erie Basin," U.S. Department of the Interior, Bureau of Commercial Fisheries, August 1968.

Appendix C
Biological and Chemical Submodels

1. R. S. Davidson and A. B. Clymer, "The Desirability and Applicability of Simulating Ecosystems," *Annals N.Y. Acad. Sciences,* 123 (Jan. 31, 1966), pp, 790–794.

2. R. B. Bird, W. E. Stewart, and E. N. Lightfoot, *Transport Phenomena* (New York: J. Wiley, 1960).

3. C. F. Prutton and S. H. Maron, *Principles of Physical Chemistry* (New York: Macmillan, 1958).

4. E. R. G. Eckert and R. M. Drake, *Heat and Mass Transfer* (New York: McGraw Hill, 1968).

Appendix E
A Method for Estimating Recreation Benefits

1. Sales Management, Inc., "Survey of Buying Power," Bill Brothers Publications, June 10, 1968.